Astro Navigation

Made Easy

Using a Pocket Calculator

François Meyrier

Translated by David Fairhall

ADLARD COLES NAUTICAL
London

Published by Adlard Coles Nautical
an imprint of A & C Black Publishers Ltd
37 Soho Square, London W1D 3QZ
www.adlardcoles.com

Copyright © Les Editions du Plaisancier 2000

First published 2003 by Adlard Coles Nautical
First published 2000 in France by Les Editions du
Plaisancier under the title *Mémento Vagnon de la
Navigation Astronomique*

ISBN 0-7136-62220

Typeset in 9 on 11pt Optima

Printed and bound in France

Note While all reasonable care has been taken in
the publication of this book, the publisher takes no
responsibility for the use of the methods or products
described in the book.

Acknowledgements
The author and publisher would like to thank the
following people and organisations for their help
with the preparation of this book and permission to
use extracts and other materials:

L'Institut de Mécanique Céleste/Bureau des longitudes:
  extracts from *Ephémérides nautiques* and
  L'Almanach du marin Breton
Her Majesty's Stationery Office: extracts from *Sight
  Reduction Tables for Air Navigation AP 3270 Vol 2*
Service Hydrographique et Océanographique de la
  Marine: extracts from charts 6955, 6688, and 7406
Casio Instruments
Agence Photo-France
Illustrations: Jacques Boutry

CONTENTS

Electronic navigation is so widely used by yachtsmen, and the equipment so reliable, one might well ask why we need another book about navigating by the sun and the stars. In just a few years, traditional methods have been swept aside by modern push-button technology, and above all by GPS. In some quarters, using a sextant to fix your position is considered old fashioned, even anachronistic.

Even these days, however, it is worthwhile having somebody on board who knows how to navigate by the traditional method. Some offshore race organisers actually insist on it.

After all, even the most reliable electronic equipment can occasionally fail. And if you do have a sextant on board, why not use it to check the position displayed by the GPS? There is great satisfaction, after plotting two or three star sights, in being able to point to the chart and declare: 'We are there!'

This book offers a fresh approach – simpler, and in our opinion more efficient than conventional methods. Using the British and American sight reduction tables AP3270 and HO249 involves a great deal of manipulation and interpolation which can cause confusion. Developed before modern

calculators were available, they have acquired their own methodology, and at times their sheer complexity can easily lead to errors.

Instead of tables, therefore, a simple pocket calculator can do the job – and it has the added advantage of reducing the cost and weight of publications you need on board. Almost any type of calculator will do, provided it can handle trigonometric functions and their reciprocals. There is no need for a programmable model, though it does help to have a function key that will convert sexagesimals (eg hours, minutes and seconds) into decimals and vice versa.

To do your own calculations you will need only basic secondary school trigonometry, and it is worth spending a bit of time brushing up that knowledge rather than ploughing through all the paperwork associated with the tabular approach. Moreover, theory should go hand-in-hand with practice, so that numerical calculations are applied directly to proven formulae. Then, if you lose your way, you can go straight back to the theory which underlies the practice.

Yet it would be wrong to ignore the sight reduction tables altogether. They are still widely used, and credit should go to those who developed and popularised a method that has been part of the maritime scene for nearly thirty years. So Chapter 13 demonstrates the principle on which they are based by working through a practical example, using the HO249 tables.

However, the central aim of this book, having first explained the rudiments of cosmography, is to help readers master the direct application of the altitude position line to the Sun, the planets and the stars (Moon sights are not covered).

Extract from chart N° 6955, Service Hydrographique et Océanographique de la Marine authorisation N° 340/2000.

This calculator is the Casio FX-115MS, but almost any calculator will do provided that it can handle trigonometric functions and their reciprocals. It does not have to be programmable, though it is extremely useful to have a function key that will convert sexagesimals (eg hours, minutes and seconds) into decimals and vice versa (see page 59).

Equipped in this way you can, if you wish, dispense with complicated sight reduction tables and do your own calculations, applying the basic principles of celestial navigation.

Chapter 1

THE SUN AND THE EARTH

THE ECLIPTIC AND THE SEASONS IN THE NORTHERN HEMISPHERE

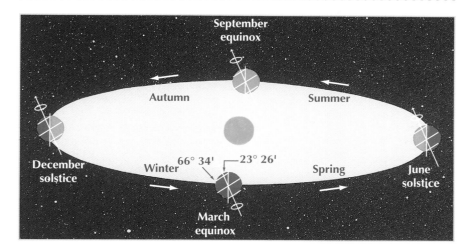

The Earth's orbit takes the form of an ellipse, one of whose foci is occupied by the Sun. The plane of this ellipse is known as the ecliptic (eclipses occur in the ecliptic plane). The planets, whose paths are also elliptical, can be considered, for navigational purposes, to move in the same ecliptic plane.

The polar axis on which the Earth rotates is not perpendicular to the ecliptic plane, but permanently inclined at an angle of 66° 34'.

The Earth moves in two ways: rotating on its own axis every 24 hours, and revolving round the Sun on average every 365.2422 solar days (365 days, 5 hours, 48 minutes and 46 seconds).

Mathematically, an ellipse is the curved shape formed by the points T, the sum of whose distances from two fixed points F1 and F2, known as foci, is constant. TF1 + TF2 = constant. A circle is an ellipse whose two foci are merged.

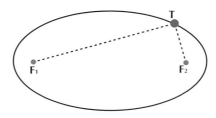

EQUINOXES

Since the Sun's rays are effectively parallel when they reach us, they can be visualised as a cylinder of light whose end forms an illuminated circle around the Earth. This circle, the division between day and night, is perpendicular to the ecliptic. At the equinoxes, the illuminated circle passes through the poles in a plane perpendicular to the equator.

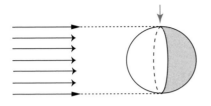

As the Earth goes round the Sun, there are two points, diametrically opposite one another, where the Sun is in the equatorial plane. These two points are known as equinoxes (from the Latin equinoxia, meaning equal night, because day and night are of equal duration) and correspond to a zero declination D of the Sun (see the definition of declination in chapter 4 Hour Angles GHA, LHA and declination D, page 27).

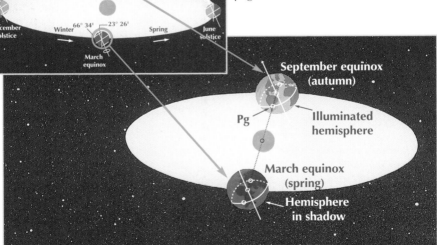

- The spring equinox, on about 20 March, marks the beginning of spring.
- The autumn equinox, on about 23 September, marks the beginning of autumn.

SOLSTICES

At two other diametrically opposite points, the line diagramatically joining the centre of the Earth to the centre of the Sun forms an angle of 23° 26′ with the plane of the equator. These two positions are known as solstices (from the Latin sol stat, meaning stationary Sun) and correspond to a solar declination D = +/- 23° 26′.

A declination (D) of + 23° 26′ corresponds to the longest day of the year, whereas D = - 23° 26′ corresponds to the shortest day.

A line joining the centres of the Earth and the Sun cuts the Earth's surface at a point Pg known as the geographical position (or the Sun's 'footprint' on Earth).

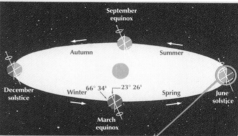

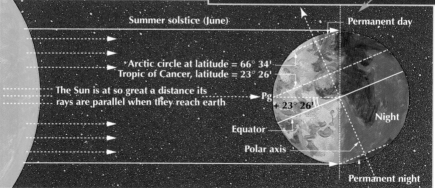

The winter solstice could be illustrated by a symmetrical (and opposite) diagram: Sun to the right and Earth to the left. Permanent night would be to the north and permanent day to the south. The Tropic of Capricorn (latitude -23° 26′) would replace the Tropic of Cancer.

- The summer solstice, around 21 June in the northern hemisphere, marks the beginning of summer.
- The winter solstice, around 22 December in the northern hemisphere, marks the beginning of winter.

A day normally means the notional time interval between successive passages of the Sun's centre across a particular meridian like Greenwich, ie 24 hours. But there is also a sidereal day (almost four minutes shorter than the solar day, because of the Earth's orbital motion) which is the interval between successive passages of a star across a given meridian.

The sidereal day does not vary. The 360° orbit is covered in 23 hours, 56 minutes and 4 seconds. But in spite of its constant duration, this day has not been adopted as a unit of time because activities on earth are obviously governed by the movement of the Sun, not the stars.

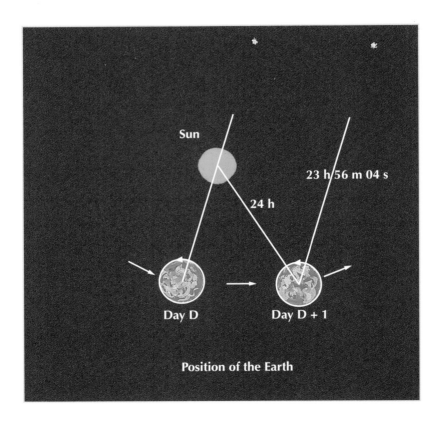

Sun

23 h 56 m 04 s

24 h

Day D   Day D + 1

Position of the Earth

KEPLER'S THREE LAWS
(the basis of the ephemerides or almanac)

Between 1605 and 1618 the German astronomer Kepler explained precisely how the solar system, conceived by Copernicus, worked, and formulated three laws to describe the movement of the planets:

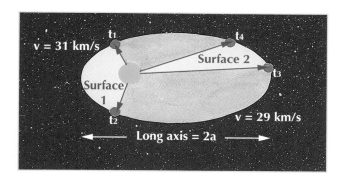

1 The Earth's orbit describes an ellipse, with the Sun at one of its foci;
2 Law of areas: the radius vector sweeps equal areas in equal times (areas are proportional to times)

$$\frac{\text{surface 1}}{t_2 - t_1} = \frac{\text{surface 2}}{t_4 - t_3}$$

3 Law of squares of orbital periods: the square of the orbital period T is proportional to the cube of half the large axis:

$$T^2/a^3 = \text{constant}$$

These three laws were completed by the laws of celestial mechanics discovered by the English mathematician Newton and published in 1687 in his celebrated book *Philosophiae Naturalis Principia Mathematica*. Thanks to the existence of these laws it is possible to predict the position of heavenly bodies to the nearest second. They are issued in an annual publication known as an almanac or ephemerides.

Since celestial navigation is based on the altitude of heavenly bodies, it is essential to know their position at the moment you measure their altitude with a sextant. With this in mind, you can understand why people often talk about a celestial mark (by analogy with landmark or sea mark).

Four times a year (usually 20 March, 21 June, 23 September and 22 December, although these dates can vary from year to year) the Sun passes an important position.

VARIATION OF THE SUN'S DECLINATION DURING THE YEAR

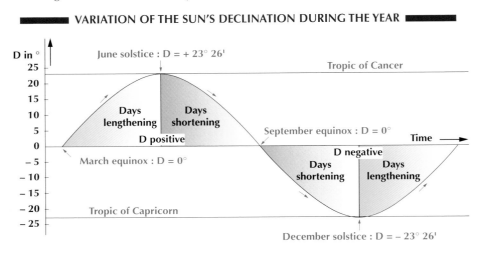

Take a careful look at the diagram above, showing the position of the Sun relative to the equator. If we draw a line between the centres of the Earth and the Sun, it cuts the Earth's surface at a point Pg known as the geographical position or footprint of the Sun. And since this position Pg is on the surface of the globe, it could be located by its latitude, as one would with a sailing ship. Instead, we use its declination D, which in this example amounts to the same thing (see page 27 for a definition of declination).

Information in this diagram can also be expressed as follows:

Mar 20 – Sep 23	Position Pg is above the equator	Declination D is positive
Sep 23 – Mar 20	Position Pg is below the equator	Declination D is negative

Jun 21 – Dec 22	Days get shorter	D decreases ie its variation is negative
Dec 22 – Jun 21	Days get longer	D increases ie its variation is positive

In other words, the Sun moves continuously between a positive declination of 23° 26' (midsummer day) and a negative declination of 23° 26' (midwinter), twice having a declination of zero (on the first days of spring and autumn). These concepts will be very useful when we come to calculate the exact declination at the moment a sextant sight is taken.

RELATIVE SIZES

Diameters compared

	Diameter in km	Diameter on a scale with Sun's diameter = 14cm
Moon	3 500	0.3 mm
Earth	12 700	1.2 mm
Sun	1 400 000	14 cm
Mars	6 700	0.6 mm
Jupiter	142 000	1.4 cm

Distances compared

	Distance in km	Distance based on distance from Earth to Sun = 15m	Time taken for light to travel between the two heavenly bodies (speed of light 300 000 km/s)
Earth - Moon	384 000	3.8 cm	1.3 sec
Sun - Earth	150 000 000	15 m	8 min
Sun - Jupiter	780 000 000	78 m	43 min
Sun - Proxima Centauri[1]	4.2 light years	4 200 km	4.2 years
Sun - Andromeda[2]	3 x 10^{19} (= 3 million light years)	3 milliard[3] km	3 million years

(1) Proxima Centauri is the nearest star to Earth.
(2) Andromeda is the only galaxy visible with the naked eye.
(3) A milliard = 1000 million.

THE SOLAR SYSTEM: VOLUMES COMPARED
(relative distances are not correct)

Light year = distance travelled by light in one year
= 300 000 km/sec x 60 sec/min x 60 min/h x 24 h/day x 365 days/year
= 10 000 milliard km
= 10^{13} km

THE SOLAR SYSTEM: ORBITS COMPARED
(relative distances are correct)

Note:
1 million = 1 000 000 = 10^6
1 milliard = 1 000 000 000 = 10^9

E = Earth
V = Venus
S = Sun

A CHRONOLOGY

A table of dates, people and their principal discovery or theory

		Person	Discovery or theory
– 600			
		Anaximander	Put Earth at centre of universe
– 500			
		Anaxagoras	Knew Earth was round
– 400			
		Heraclitus of Pont	Realised Earth rotates
– 300			
		Aristarchus of Samos	Understood that Earth orbits the Sun (rediscovered 18 centuries later)
	– 230	Erastosthenes	Measured Earth's circumference to within 10 per cent
– 200			
			Measured length of year
			Discovered precession of equinoxes
– 100		Hipparchus	Measured distance between Earth and Moon
			Published map of stars
			Invented trigonometry
0			
			Devised geocentric system
	150	Ptolemy	Produced map of stars
200			Published Almagest in Latin (retranslated into Arabic about 1200)
	1252	King of Castille	Published Alphonsine tables
	1492	Christopher Colombus	Discovered America
1500			
	1543	Copernicus	Understood that world is heliocentric
	1572	Tycho-Brahe	Collected observations
	1584	Giordano Bruno	Suggested that other solar systems might exist (for which he was burnt at the stake)
1600			
			Deduced that Earth and planets have elliptical orbits
	1609	Kepler	Formulated law of areas
			Formulated law of squares of orbital periods
	1610	Galileo	Discovered Jupiter's satellites
			Developed telescope bearing his name
	1614	Neper	Invented logarithms
	1656	Huygens	Made clock pendulum
	1687	Newton	Discovered laws of planetary motion and differential calculus; invented a telescope
1700			
	1731	Hadley	Invented octant and sextant
	1765	Harrison	Built H4 chronometer to win longitude prize
1800			
	1837	Sumner	Accidentally discovered altitude position line
	1846	Le Verrier	Discovered planet Neptune by calculation alone
	1875	Adml. Marcq de Saint-Hilaire	Formulated theory of altitude position line
In modern times			Consol, Loran, Decca, Satnav, then GPS

■ THE MARINE QUADRANT ■

Gunter's marine quadrant is made from a quarter circle of wood, brass or copper graduated, like a protractor, from 0 to 90°. The star is sighted across the two projections. Altitude is given directly by reading off where the plumb line crosses the scale along the curved edge. The quadrant was in use from about 1450 to 1650 (200 years). The reference is the vertical plumb line.

■ JACOB'S STAFF ■

Jacob's staff (or cross-staff) is attributed to Levy ben Gerson. It consists of a piece of wood, like the head of a mallet, sliding along a staff graduated in degrees. It was in use from the end of the fifteenth to the end of the eighteenth century (300 years). Four heads of different sizes can be used. Altitudes are read directly from the four graduated sides of the staff. The reference is the horizon.

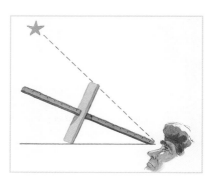

A marine astrolabe is made from thick bronze, cut away to reduce windage. It was in use from 1450 to 1800 (350 years). The base is solid metal so that it hangs vertically (like a plumb line). You line up the star through the two sighting holes on the movable alidade and read the zenith distance directly from the graduated scale. The assembly hangs from a ring that is free to move in any direction. One hundred astrolabes still exist throughout the world; there are five in the UK, four of which are at the National Maritime Museum, Greenwich.

A kamal is a small rectangular wooden board with a notch in the centre of one side. A fixed length of cord is stretched between the observer's teeth and the middle of the board. This extremely simple instrument appeared in the Middle Ages and was still in use in 1875 in the Indian Ocean. It is adjusted to match the altitude of the Pole Star at the destination port. This makes it possible to navigate along a parallel of latitude (the cord has several knots for different latitudes).

None of these instruments is accurate to more than a degree, that is 60 nautical miles (or 111 km)

Chapter 2

THE SEXTANT

THE SEXTANT SIMPLY MEASURES ANGLES

The modern sextant, made of metal or thick plastic, is a precision optical instrument enabling you to measure the angle between two rays of light. Its main use is to establish the height (or altitude) of heavenly bodies above the horizon, as measured in degrees, minutes and tenths of a minute. The angle it measures is formed by two sight lines – one from the observer's eye to the horizon, and the other up to the heavenly body.

In simple terms, therefore, a sextant is like a protractor. But it is so precise, that its accuracy is limited in practice by the human eye's ability to differentiate, which when taking a sight from a sailing boat is about one minute of arc.

As we shall see (pages 18 & 19), from this angular measurement we can immediately deduce the distance in miles between the observer and a point directly beneath the heavenly body. So in this sense, the sextant is also a device for measuring distance.

HOW THE SEXTANT WORKS

A sextant is assembled from the following components:

Two mirrors: an index mirror, which reflects rays of light from the heavenly body towards the horizon mirror; and the horizon mirror, which reflects the same rays of light towards the observer's eye; this horizon mirror **2** (in which you sight the heavenly body) is adjacent to a pane of transparent glass **1** (to view the horizon);

Two sets of shades: in front of each mirror is a set of three to five shades, or filters of tinted glass, to reduce the amount of light reaching the observer's eye;

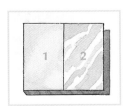

A movable index arm with, at its end, a cylindrical adjustment screw graduated – depending on the model – in tenths or two tenths of a minute of arc.

A frame, the curved base of which forms an arc of a circle, graduated in degrees, with a telescope attached at the side.

Because the images being sighted are doubly reflected, the angle measured along the arc by moving the index arm is halved (so that although the arc forms only a sixth of a circle, 60°, it is actually graduated from 0° to 120°).

The mirrors are perpendicular to the plane of the instrument.

The telescope optical axis is parallel to the plane of the instrument.

Filters and drum are not shown on the drawings below.

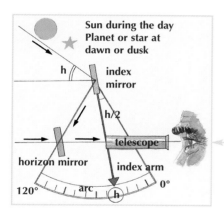

Sun during the day
Planet or star at dawn or dusk

h

index mirror

h/2

telescope

horizon mirror

index arm

120°   arc   0°

h

View through the telescope when sighting the lower edge or limb of the Sun, or a star.

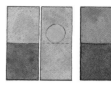

To measure the altitude, you lower the Sun or the star on to the horizon by 'opening' the index arm.

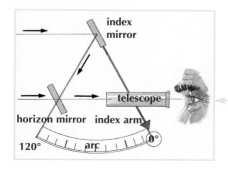

index mirror

telescope

horizon mirror   index arm

120°   arc   0°

View through the telescope when the sextant is adjusted to 0° 0'

Horizon viewed twice

On a correctly adjusted sextant, the direct and reflected images line up on a common horizon.

Never, ever, look at the sun with naked eyes, always use filters.

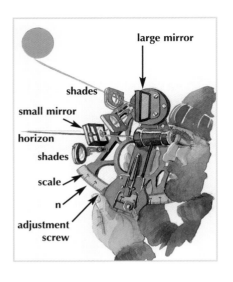

large mirror

shades

small mirror

horizon
shades

scale

n

adjustment
screw

FOUR STAGES IN TAKING A SIGHT

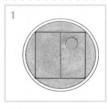

1 Insert the shades, turn the adjustment screw to 0°, and sight the Sun.

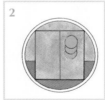

2 Open the sextant so as to 'drop' the image of the Sun down towards the horizon.

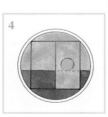

3 Turn the adjustment screw until the Sun's lower edge (limb) touches the horizon

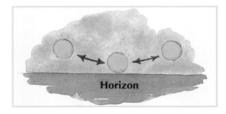

Horizon

(and swing the sextant gently from side to side so the Sun just brushes the horizon).

4 When the Sun is touching the horizon, immediately note the time of the sight to the nearest second (at the equator, an error of 4 seconds results in an error of one mile in the geographical position Pg of the Sun).

To convert the sextant altitude *Hs* measured on the sextant to the true altitude Ho of the Sun, we must apply six corrections:
- The correction Ci of the index error *e*;
- The four angular corrections, including dip, (table *g*, page 17);
- The calendar correction (only for the Sun – table *c*, page 17).

■■■■ CORRECTION Ci OF THE INDEX ERROR *e* ■■■■
(this error is peculiar to each sextant)

Set the sextant to 0° 00′ ie put the index arm at 0° on the arc and the adjustment screw at 00′. Sight the horizon (or an object more than three miles away). One of these two images will appear, and an appropriate correction must be applied.

Move the adjustment screw one way or the other until the two half-images coincide.

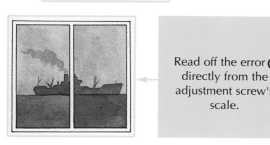

Read off the error *e* directly from the adjustment screw's scale.

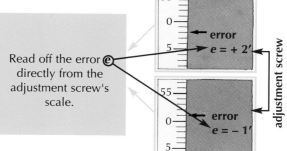

Numerically, the correction Ci of the index error *e* has the same value as the error, but with the opposite sign: Ci = - *e*. So if the index error *e* = +2′, then the correction Ci = - 2′; if the index error *e* = -1′, then the correction Ci = + 1′.

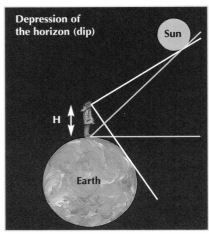

Depression of the horizon (dip)

The diagram shows how measurements depend on the height of the eye H above the horizon. The greater the height H, the more important it is to make allowance for it. Hence the need for a first angular correction, for depression or dip.

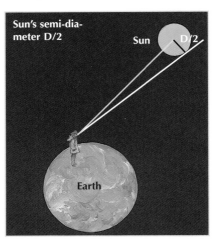

Sun's semi-diameter D/2

Measurements are supposed in principle to be taken from the centre of heavenly bodies. But in the case of the Sun (whose apparent semi-diameter D/2 = 16′) this is impractical, and we generally sight the lower edge (or limb) and make an appropriate adjustment. Hence the second angular correction.

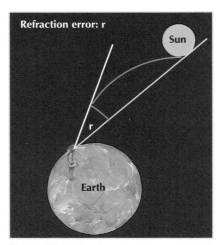

Refraction error: r

Rays of light bend as they pass through different layers in the atmosphere. In other words the light reaching the Earth from heavenly bodies is subject to refraction, shown here as r. For this we need a third correction.

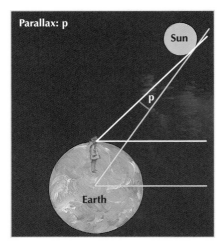

Parallax: p

Altitude sights are theoretically taken from the centre of the Earth, but of course in reality from its surface. This requires the fourth correction, for parallax.

g) **Altitude of the Sun's lower limb**.

Four corrections grouped together in a single correction Cg, expressed in minutes of arc (ie refraction – dip + parallax + semi-diameter);

sextant alti-tude hi	0 m	2 m	EYE LEVEL 4 m	6 m	8 m	10 m
10° 00′	10.8	8.3	7.3	6.5	5.8	5.2
° 20′	11.0	8.5	7.4	6.6	5.9	5.3
° 40′	11.2	8.6	7.6	6.8	6.1	5.5
11° 00′	11.3	8.8	7.7	6.9	6.3	5.7
° 30′	11.5	9.0	7.9	7.1	6.5	5.9
12° 00′	11.7	9.2	8.1	7.3	6.7	6.1
° 30′	11.9	9.4	8.3	7.5	6.8	6.2
13° 00′	12.0	9.5	8.5	7.7	7.0	6.4
° 30′	12.2	9.7	8.6	7.8	7.1	6.5
14° 00′	12.3	9.8	8.8	8.0	7.3	6.7
15° 00′	12.6	10.1	9.0	8.2	7.5	6.9
16° 00′	12.8	10.3	9.3	8.5	7.8	7.2
17° 00′	13.0	10.5	9.5	8.7	8.0	7.4
18° 00′	13.2	10.7	9.6	8.8	8.2	7.6
19° 00′	13.4	10.8	9.8	9.0	8.3	7.7
20° 00′	13.5	11.0	9.9	9.1	8.5	7.9
22° 00′	13.8	11.3	10.2	9.4	8.7	8.1
24° 00′	14.0	11.5	10.4	9.6	8.9	8.3
26° 00′	14.2	11.7	10.6	9.8	9.1	8.5
28° 00′	14.3	11.8	10.8	10.0	9.3	8.7
30° 00′	14.5	12.0	10.9	10.1	9.4	8.8
32° 00′	14.6	12.1	11.0	10.2	9.6	9.0
34° 00′	14.7	12.2	11.1	10.3	9.7	9.1
36° 00′	14.8	12.3	11.2	10.4	9.8	9.2
38° 00′	14.9	12.4	11.3	10.5	9.9	9.3
40° 00′	15.0	12.5	11.4	10.6	10.0	9.4
45° 00′	15.1	12.6	11.6	10.8	10.1	9.5
50° 00′	15.3	12.8	11.7	10.9	10.3	9.7
55° 00′	15.4	12.9	11.9	11.1	10.4	9.8
60° 00′	15.5	13.0	12.0	11.2	10.5	9.9
70° 00′	15.7	13.2	12.2	11.4	10.7	10.1

c) **Altitude of the Sun's lower limb:** calendar correction Cc (each month has a value)

January	0′.3
February	0′.2
March	0′.1
April	0′
May	– 0′.2
June	– 0′.2
July	– 0′.2
August	– 0′.2
September	– 0′.1
October	0′.1
November	0′.2
December	0′.3

Note: these tables are not suitable for Moon sights

True altitude Ho is obtained by applying the three corrections Ci, Cg and Cc to the sextant altitude Hs.
Sextant altitude Hs + index error Ci + grouped corrections Cg + calendar correction Cc = true altitude Ho.

Ho = Hs + Ci + Cg + Cc

Example: On 21 January, a sight is taken of the Sun's lower limb; the sextant shows an altitude Hs = 19° 3'.45; the index error is - 2.6'; the eye is 2 m above the horizon:

Sextant altitude	**Hs**	=	19° 03'.45
Index error correction	**Ci**	=	2'.6
Grouped corrections	**Cg**	=	10'.8
Calendar correction	**Cc**	=	0'.3
True altitude	**Ho**	=	**19° 17'.15**

The observed, or apparent altitude **Ha** is defined as follows: **Ha = Hs + Ci**

SIMPLIFIED TABLE

Corrections simplified
Applicable from a height of **2 m**

to the **Sun** -----	to **Planets**
using lower limb	and **Stars**

7° 30'	↓	↓
	7'	– 9'
9°		
	8'	– 8'
11°		
	9'	– 7'
13°		
	10'	– 6'
18°		
	11'	– 5'
27°		
	12'	– 4'
45°		
	13'	– 3'
90°		

For sights taken from a height of 2m, you can use this simplified table where the calendar correction Cc is ignored. You could usefully stick a copy of the table in the sextant's case.

THE SEXTANT ALLOWS YOU TO MEASURE DISTANCES

■■■■■■■ **FIRST EXAMPLE, borrowed from coastal navigation** ■■■■■■■

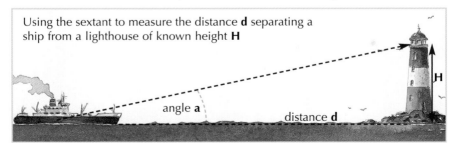

Using the sextant to measure the distance **d** separating a ship from a lighthouse of known height **H**

angle **a**

distance **d**

H

We know that if **a** is the angle measured by the sextant, then
tg a = H (metres) / **d** (miles), therefore **d** (miles) = **H** (metres) / **tg a**.

d (miles) = $\dfrac{\textbf{H} \text{ (metres)}}{1852 \times \textbf{tg a}}$ exact formula

Example 1: if **H** = 62 m
and **a** = 32° 12'.8
then **d** = 0.053 miles

d (miles) = $\dfrac{\textbf{H} \text{ (metres)} \times 1.86}{\textbf{a} \text{ (minutes)}}$ approximate formula (only applicable if **a** < 8°)

Example 2: if **H** = 12 miles
and **a** = 2° 54'.7,
then **d** = 0.127 miles

■■■■■■■■■■ **SECOND EXAMPLE, the basis of celestial navigation** ■■■■■■■■■

The sextant measures the height of the Sun's lower limb above the horizon.

The important thing to note here, as shown in the diagram below, is that the zenith distance **zd** = 90° – **H**, expressed in minutes of arc, is also a measure of the distance in nautical miles between the observer and the heavenly body's footprint Pg.

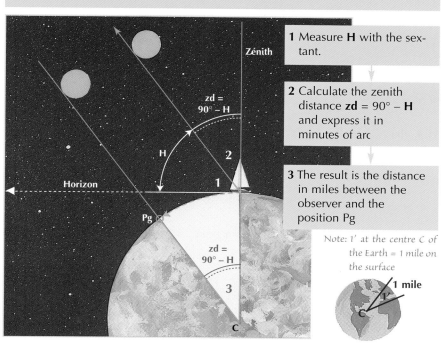

Zénith

zd = 90° – H

H   2

Horizon   1

Pg

zd = 90° – H

3

C

1 Measure **H** with the sextant.

2 Calculate the zenith distance **zd** = 90° – **H** and express it in minutes of arc

3 The result is the distance in miles between the observer and the position Pg

Note: 1' at the centre C of the Earth = 1 mile on the surface

1 mile

Example: if **H** = 32° 12'.8, then **zd** = 90° – **H**,
zd = 90° – 32° 12'.8 = 57° 47'.2 = (57° x 60') + 47'.2 = 3467'.2.
Thus, 3467.2 miles separate the observer from the geographical position **Pg** of the heavenly body.

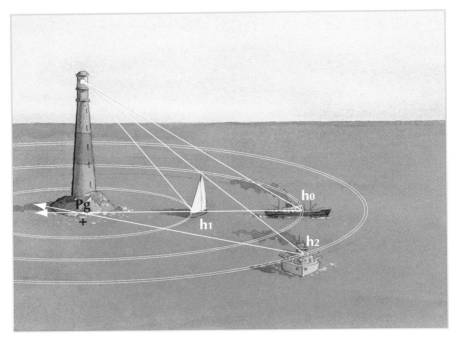

From the cargo ship, the lighthouse is at an elevation **ho**:

- if observation gives an angle **h1**, where **h1** > **ho**, the sailing yacht is nearer **Pg** than the cargo ship;
- if observation gives an angle **h2**, where **h2** < **ho**, the cruiser is further from **Pg** than the cargo ship.

The three circles represent three geometrical positions. From any point on a given circle, the lighthouse will be seen at a constant elevation.

By convention, the axes Ship – > Base of the lighthouse **Pg** are orientated positively from the ships to the base of the lighthouse.

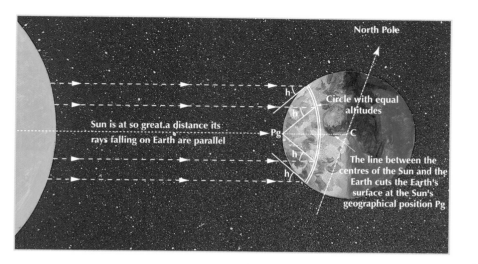

North Pole

Circle with equal altitudes

Sun is at so great a distance its rays falling on Earth are parallel

Pg

C

The line between the centres of the Sun and the Earth cuts the Earth's surface at the Sun's geographical position Pg

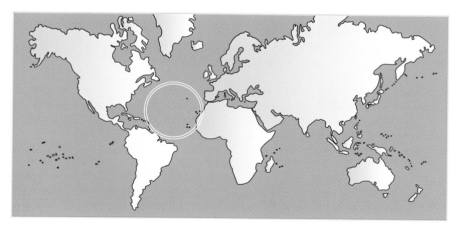

When a position circle is extremely large (as it usually will be when the lighthouse is replaced by the Sun), and when **h** < 80°, a curved section of it is treated as a straight line called an altitude position line.

Chapter 3

TIME

THE REAL SUN

The real Sun is above our heads, and it is a very bad indicator of time because its movement is irregular. Real solar time is the hour angle (see Hour Angles GHA, LHA and declination D, page 27) of the real Sun (the angle is 0° when the Sun crosses the observer's meridian).

THE MEAN SUN AND THE WATCH

The mean Sun is an imaginary Sun, supposedly moving at a steady rate so as to average out the real Sun's movement (like the regular movement of a quartz watch). Mean solar time is the hour angle of the mean Sun.

The mean Sun and the real Sun make the same number of passages across our sky in a year, but the real Sun is sometimes ahead, and sometimes behind, the mean Sun. The time difference between the two Suns is known as the equation of time. This difference can be as much as 16 minutes!

UNIVERSAL TIME AND THE TIME OF PASSAGE

Universal time UT is mean solar time at Greenwich + 12h. The time of passage T Pass (also known at the Sun's meridian passage) is the UT at which the real Sun is above the Greenwich meridian.

UT can be obtained from:

- The speaking clock
- GPS, which in addition to its positioning function, also displays UT
- Watches equipped to receive the time signal of the atomic clock in Frankfurt (whose range is 1,500 km)

- Periodic time signals broadcast on short wave; the broadcast frequencies are given in marine radionavigation publications.

A highly accurate quartz watch is essential to maintain UT. But however accurate it is, there will always be some difference between UT and the time shown by the watch. To keep track of this, and to control it, you need to record the difference every 24 hours, together with the rate at which it changes.

See pages 107 to 113

THE EQUATION OF TIME

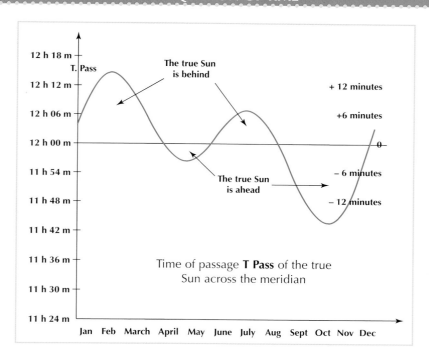

On 1 April in the year N, the Sun crosses the Greenwich meridian at 12h 03m 51s, which means that the real Sun is 3m 51s behind the (imaginary) mean Sun.

Important note

From now on, to make it easier to calculate fractions, we shall always convert sexagesimal times (ie hours, minutes and seconds) into decimals (for the method, see the section 'How to convert sexagesimal into decimal data', page 59). For instance, the decimal equivalent of 12h

03m 51s is 12.06416h, or even better 12h.06416. And the same applies to degrees of arc expressed in sexagesimals, which will also be converted into decimals.

Even though it is not absolutely correct to express times and degrees in decimals, for convenience they will therefore be written as follows:

22h 38m → 22h.63333
10° 52′ → 10°.86667

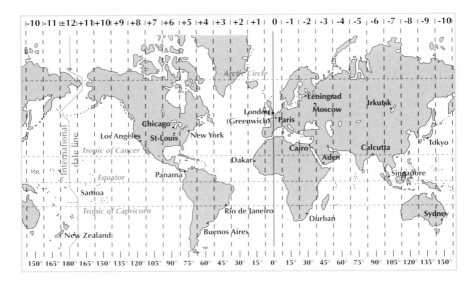

As soon as you travel any substantial distance from the Greenwich meridian, you must change your time if you want the Sun to reach its highest point at about your local midday.

The Washington Convention of 1883 established the principle of changing local time by adding or subtracting complete hours to or from UT, with the Greenwich meridian as zero. So wherever you are in the world, clocks show the same minutes and hours, differing only in the number of complete hours. Yet a few countries do not use the complete hour system.

The globe is divided into 24 time zones, each covering 15° of longitude, numbered from 0 to 23, with each country generally choosing for its local time the zone containing its political capital.

The Greenwich Royal Observatory is at the centre of the time zone 0.

Chapter 4

SPHERICAL CO-ORDINATES

Although celestial navigation deals with the Sun and the distant stars, it has no practical purpose unless their movement can be related to our position here on Earth. Navigators therefore make a number of artificial working assumptions, generally dealing with the world as it appears, rather than how it actually works.

They envisage our spherical Earth at the centre of another, concentric sphere – the celestial sphere – forming the sky across which the various heavenly bodies appear to move. This construct has the enormous advantage that any system of co-ordinates which establishes a position on Earth, or on the celestial sphere, can be transferred from one to the other. The trigonometry of the various triangles is the same in either case.

GEOGRAPHICAL (TERRESTRIAL) CO-ORDINATES

Geographical co-ordinates enable navigators to define and locate any position on land or sea.

The terrestrial globe is divided up by parallel planes of latitude, L, perpendicular to the polar axis, and by meridians of longitude, G, which are semi-circles joining the north and south poles.

They are located by reference to the Greenwich meridian and the equator. Counting from these as zero, the convention is as follows:

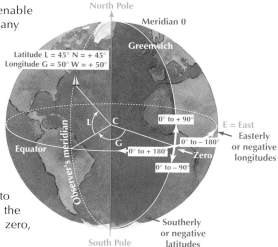

- Longitudes 0 to 180° W are positive, ie G = 0° to + 180°; longitudes 0 to 180° E are negative, ie G = 0° to -180°;
- Latitudes 0 to 90° N are positive, ie L = 0 to + 90°; and latitudes 0 to 90° S are negative, ie L = 0° to -90°.

Examples

	L = 49° 00′.9	N = 49°.015
NE Minquiers buoy in the Channel:	G = 1° 55′.2	W = 1°.92
Cap d'Armes Lt on Ile de Porquerolles:	L = 45° 59′.0	N = 45°.98333
	G = 6° 12′.4	E = -6°.20666

Just as angular measurements of latitude and longitude directly define our position on Earth, or on a chart, measurements of height and bearing can define it relative to a nearby lighthouse or a distant star.

With the observer at Z, the aim is to establish the relative position of a heavenly body, or mark.

- A vertical line from the observer's position cuts the celestial sphere at the *zenith Z.*

- The plane perpendicular to this line at the observer's level is the *local horizon.*
- The *heavenly body's vertical plane* contains that body, the observer, and the zenith Z.
- The *altitude of the heavenly body* is the angle formed within this plane by the line ZA and the horizon.
- The *azimuth Z,* also known as the *true* bearing Zv or true azimuth Az, is the angle between the vertical planes of the north pole and the heavenly body.

The azimuth Z is numbered from 0 to 360°, starting from N.
The altitude H is numbered from 0 to 90°, starting from the horizon.

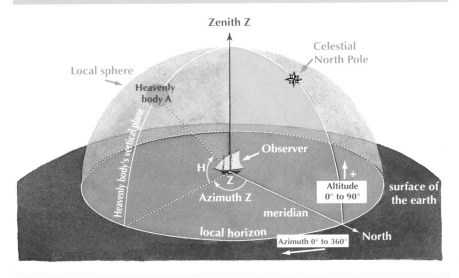

Example 1
In the Irish Sea, I take a compass bearing, 355°, of the Fastnet lighthouse, and measure its height as 3°.

Example 2
On 23 May in the year N+1, at 11h 27m 16s UT, as sighted from the Ile de Sein the Sun has an azimuth of 156° and an altitude of 60°.6. On the same day at the same time, the Sun as seen from Saint-Mandrier has an azimuth of 177° and an altitude of 67°.2.

(This second example is a reminder that these co-ordinates depend on the observer's position, so two observers will simultaneously take different bearings of the same heavenly body.)

- Notice that the azimuth involved here is numbered from the north; it must not be confused with the azimuth used in astronomy, which is numbered from the south.

- Z designates the observer's position and his zenith, as well as the true bearing of the heavenly body.

HOUR ANGLES GHA, LHA AND DECLINATION D

These co-ordinates, which are similar to longitude and latitude on Earth, enable you to define the position of any body moving through the sky (Sun or planets), or of any fixed star. The centre of the celestial sphere can be visualised as being either at the observer's eye or at the centre of the Earth. In this illustration, the Earth is supposedly stationary at the centre of the diagram.

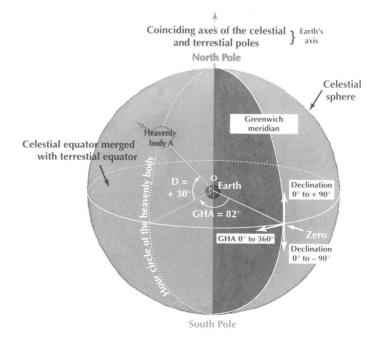

The *hour circle of a heavenly body* is the semi-circle containing the body and the earth's axis.

The first co-ordinate is the *Greenwich hour angle* ie the angle between the Greenwich meridian and the heavenly body's hour circle.

The second co-ordinate, the angle between the line OA and the equatorial plane, is the *declination* (equivalent to latitude).

Greenwich hour angle GHA is numbered from 0 to 360° in a westerly direction from the Greenwich meridian.

Declination D is measured from 0 to 90°, with a positive sign + to the north and a negative sign – to the south.

An almanac such as the *Ephémérides Nautiques*, or the *Nautical Almanac*, gives these angles for the Sun and the planets, as well as for an imaginary position known as the First Point of Aries (the position of the Sun on 20 or 21 March, depending on the year, at the moment its declination is zero). As we shall see, the stars are located by reference to this First Point of Aries.

The speed of the Sun's geographical position on Earth:
- The Sun completes one complete circuit of 360° in 24 hours;
- 360° divided by 24 equals 15° in an hour (or 15° x 60 x 1.852 kilometres per hour = 1666 kph = 462 metres a second at the equator).
- In other words, at the equator it moves one mile in four seconds.

■■■■■■■■ TIME CO-ORDINATES ON THE TERRESTRIAL SPHERE: ■■■■■■■■
the local hour angle LHA

Since the terrestrial and celestial spheres have the same centre, GHA can be represented directly on the Earth, as in the diagram below. The local hour angle LHA is the angle between the observer's meridian and the meridian of the heavenly body.

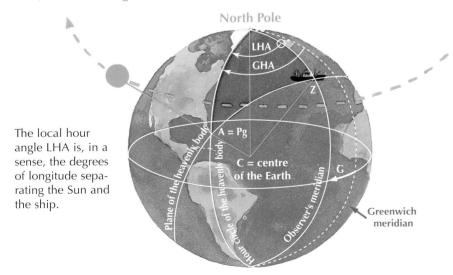

The local hour angle LHA is, in a sense, the degrees of longitude separating the Sun and the ship.

In order to show the local hour angle LHA above, we have also illustrated – anticipating later chapters – *the famous triangle ZPA* (where Z is the observer on his ship). The triangle is formed by sections of three great circles, cutting one another at Z, P and A (a great circle round a sphere is a circle whose plane passes through the centre of the sphere).

Notation

We always use the abbreviations GHA and LHA for hour angles, but in some publications readers will encounter a different notation when referring to the Sun, where AHvo is equivalent to GHA and AHvg to LHA.

Note that when the Sun reaches its highest point above the horizon, its corresponding position Pg is on the observer's meridian (and hour circle).

Another way of looking at it

From the deck of your anchored vessel, you observe that the Sun:

- Rises in the east;
- Reaches its highest point at midday, real local time, on your meridian;
- Sets in the west.

Strictly speaking, this is only true at the equinoxes; at other times of year the Sun does not rise exactly in the east, or set exactly in the west.

At midday, real local time, the two planes (the hour circle of the Sun and your meridian) coincide, so LHA = 0. As time passes, the local hour angle increases to 1°, 2°...15°...30°...

- 90° (the Sun disappears in the west)....
- 180° (midnight, real local time, and the Sun is diametrically opposite you)
- 270° (it is dawn, and the Sun reappears in the east),

until finally, the Sun completes its circuit of the Earth...350°...360°. The Sun is once more at its highest; it is the next day, midday real local time, and again LHA= 0.

▬▬▬ THE RELATIONSHIP BETWEEN LHA (local hour angle) AND GHA ▬▬▬
(hour angle at Greenwich meridian)

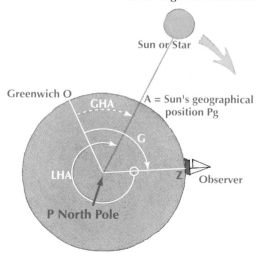

The footprint (or trace) of the heavenly body on the Earth is the position Pg. The observer is on his boat at Z. The arc OZ represents the longitude G of the position Z. The arc OA marks out the heavenly body's Greenwich hour angle GHA, measured from the Greenwich meridian.

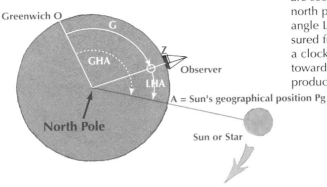

The positions Z, P and A are seen here from the north pole. The local hour angle LHA (always measured from the observer in a clockwise direction towards the heavenly body) produces the arc ZA.

A = Sun's geographical position Pg

Applying the Chasles relationship to the points O, Z and A, then the arc OA = OZ + ZA, which means that GHA = G + LHA. It will always be the case, therefore, that LHA = GHA - G.

Example
To find the value of LHA at 5° 56' E = -5°.93333 on 4th May in the year N, at 0h UT.

According to the almanac:

$$
\begin{array}{lll}
\text{GHA} & = 180°\ 48'.0 & = 180°.8 \\
\text{- G} & = & +\ \underline{5°.93333} \\
\text{LHA} & = & 186°.73333
\end{array}
$$

━━━━━━━━ **CALCULATING HOUR ANGLE AND DECLINATION** ━━━━━━━━
(at the exact moment the sight is taken)

An almanac is a book containing 'ephemerides', ie the tabulated position of heavenly bodies at any given time. The *Ephémérides Nautiques* is an annual almanac published by the French Bureau de Longitudes. In it you will find the hour angle and declination of the Sun, as well as the four planets used in navigation, for every hour UT of every day. It also gives the hour angle of the First Point of Aries, and the equatorial co-ordinates of all the stars.

An almanac of some kind (such as the British *Nautical Almanac*), is an essential reference if you want to find your position from the stars and the planets.

Extracts from this Ephémérides can be found in *L'Almanach du Marin Breton* (see extracts in Annexes). This almanac has one entry a day, for the Sun only, at 0h UT. The hourly variation of the hour angle, and the declination are in decimals, which is very useful.

So, on 2 January, N+1, the hour angle of the Sun at 0h UT measured from the Greenwich meridian 0 is written as AHvo, or more usually GHA. Its value, according to the almanac, is 179° 03′.6 = 179°.06, and the Sun's declination D at this same instant = 22° 57′ S = -22°.95.

One of the problems of celestial navigation is knowing these values for the precise moment the sextant sight is taken.

The following three examples show how to go about it.

Example 1

To find the value of GHA and D for the Sun at 8h 32m 55s on 2 January in the year N+1:

On this 2 January, N+1, at 0h UT, according to the almanac, the Sun's GHA and declination are as shown below:

GHA = 179° 03′.6   **hourly variation of GHA = 14°.995**
D   = 22° 57′ S   **hourly variation of D = + 0′.2**

Given the values at 0h UT, it is easy to calculate the equivalent values at 8h 32m 55s by linear interpolation (in the printed matrices *pp* stands for proportional part), ie by applying the mathematical technique known as the rule of three.

To make the calculation easier, start by converting the values into decimals:

GHA = 179°.06   **hourly variation of GHA = 14°.995**
D   = -22°.95   **hourly variation of D = + 0 2/60′ = + 0°.00333**

Notice that D has a negative sign since the declination is south (it is winter), but as the days are getting longer (2 January is between 22 December and 21 June), the hourly variation in D has a positive sign.

The values of GHA and D at 8h 32m 55s = 8h.54861:

GHA = 179°.06 + (8.54861 x 14°.995) = 307°.2464
D   = -22°.95 + (8.54861 x 0°.00333) = -22°.92153

This procedure can be laid out in a matrix designed for this particular calculation but applicable in principle to any other example:

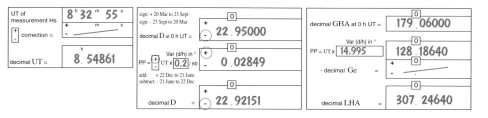

Example 2

To find the value of LHA (local hour angle) on 9 September in the year N+1 at 9h 22m 1s UT.

Since we are now dealing with the local hour angle, we must define our position, which is:

L = 3° 27'.25 S
G = 8° 8'.32 W

This time we shall work directly in the matrix, with values taken from the almanac:

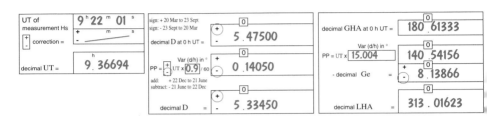

Example 3

On 24 September in the year N+1, at 18h 1m 7s, find the value of LHA and D at position:

L = 42° 06'.8 N
G = 6° 31'.8 E

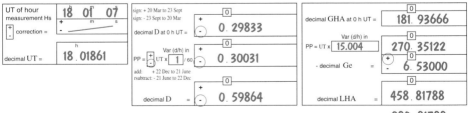

Notes

To save time, D and GHA, taken from the ephemerides in sexagesimals, are written straight into the form in decimals.

Since the longitude is east, and therefore negative, G has a negative sign and -G is positive.

The LHA may well work out at more than 360°, but this does not affect the trigonometry. Write it as: LHA-360°, or LHA -(n x 360°).

Example 3 shows that latitude plays no part in calculating the local hour angle.

THE RELATIONSHIP BETWEEN HORIZONTAL CO-ORDINATES AND TIME CO-ORDINATES

As we have seen, the Sun does not move in a haphazard fashion. On the contrary, its movements – and hence its co-ordinates at any particular instant – are known in advance. Thanks to Kepler's laws and the various almanacs published each year giving the Sun's time co-ordinates (ie the Greenwich hour angle GHA and the declination D), its position can always be accurately determined. And if the Sun's movements can be determined by reference to Greenwich, we can also predict its position relative to any other point on Earth for which we have the latitude L and the longitude G.

Time co-ordinates GHA and D
+
Geographical co-ordinates L and G

⇨   ⇨   Horizontal (local) co-ordinates

In other words, supposing that on 23 May in the year N, at 16h 03m 58s UT, you are at latitude L = 33° 25min.8 N, longitude G = 8° 0min.9 W, you can use the system of horizontal (or local) co-ordinates to give the Sun's altitude and bearing.

This approach leads directly to the concept of the *altitude position line*. We locate ourselves geometrically by comparing our calculated position with our observed position, a procedure which involves solving a simple mathematical problem.

Later in the book (see Applying the Position Triangle, page 40) we show how to transfer from time co-ordinates to local (horizontal) co-ordinates by applying two formulae derived directly from the position triangle.

The local co-ordinates, ie the angles Hc and Zc (calculated altitude and calculated bearing or azimuth), are obtained by using their sine and cosine in the following two formulae:

$$\sin Hc = \sin L \sin D + \cos L \cos D \cos LHA$$

and Zc =

angle Z: if $180° < LHA < 360°$, ie if the heavenly body is to the E

$$\cos \text{ angle } Z = \frac{\sin D - \sin L \sin Hc}{\cos L \cos Hc}$$

$360° - Z$ if $0° < LHA < 180°$ ie if heavenly body is to W

Example

On 23 May in the year N, at 16h 03m 58s UT, starting from the time co-ordinates of the Sun provided by the almanac we have worked out the following local co-ordinates:

GHA at 0h UT = 180° 49'.9   D at 0h UT = 20° 32'.5

pp	=	14°.999/h x 16h 03m 58s
- G	=	-8° 00'.9
LHA	=	413°.79226
	=	413° 47'.53 = 53° 47'.53

pp = (0.5/60)°/h x 16h 03m 58s
D = 20°.67555 = 20° 40'.53

From position L = 33° 25'.8 N, G = 8° 00'.9 W, we can obtain, without any observation, the Sun's position from its calculated altitude Hc and its calculated bearing Zc:

sin Hc = sin 33° 25'.8 x sin 20°.67555 + cos 33° 25'.8 x cos 20°.67555 x cos 53°.79226

= 0.65575 ⟶ so that Hc = 40° 58'.58

cos angle Z = $\frac{\sin 20°.67555 - \sin 33° 25'.8 \times \sin 40° 58'.57}{\cos 33° 25'.8 \times \cos 40° 58'.57}$

= - 0.01299, therefore angle Z = 90° 44min.65

and since LHA = 53° 47'.43 < 180° ⟶ therefore Zc = 360° - 90° 44'.65
= 269° 15'.35

So, the Sun's position works out as Hc = 40° 58'.58 and Zc = 269° 15'.35.

Centuries ago, people thought the stars never moved relative to one another, and were somehow attached to a celestial sphere. The daily rhythm of the skies was believed to be caused by the movement of this sphere from east to west.

For some practical purposes, this concept of the universe is still in use today. Catalogues of the stars give each of them a more or less fixed position within the celestial sphere – the sphere of the fixed stars.

In reality, the individual stars are moving, but they are so far away that the angles between them appear constant. So if you look at the position of Arcturus throughout the year N=1, you will find little change: just 0min.2 variation in the declination, and 0min.6 in the sidereal hour angle.

Our calculations will nevertheless take account of these slight movements, whose equatorial co-ordinates are published for every second month (no interpolation is needed between the two months).

The First Point of Aries S or γ (the Sun's position in the celestial vault on 20 March at the moment when its declination is nil ie at the instant spring begins) serves as zero (the starting point) for these co-ordinates, which are similar to longitude and latitude on Earth.

The hour angle of the First Point of Aries (also known as sidereal time) is counted from the Greenwich meridian and written as GHA γ (or Ahso in the French almanac: s for the First Point of Aries; o for the Greenwich meridian).

Unlike the Sun, the First Point of Aries moves at a constant speed: hourly variation GHA $\gamma = 15° \ 2'.5 = 15°.04166$.

The local hour angle of the stars is written as LHA* (it can also be written as Ahag or AH*g, where a stands for a heavenly body and * for a star).

The axis $\overrightarrow{(PS; \ PN)}$ is the axis of the celestial poles with the axis of the terrestrial poles passing through it. The plane of the celestial equator is perpendicular to it (this plane includes the terrestrial equator's plane).

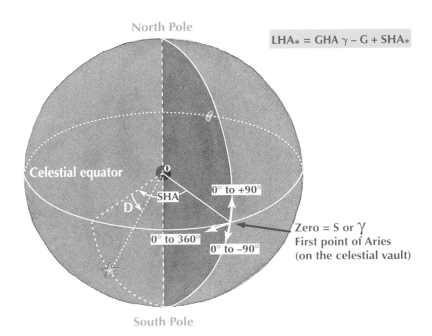

North Pole

$$LHA_* = GHA\ \gamma - G + SHA_*$$

Celestial equator

SHA

$0°$ to $+90°$

D

$0°$ to $360°$

$0°$ to $-90°$

Zero = S or γ
First point of Aries
(on the celestial vault)

South Pole

Example
On 1 January in the year N+1 (see Extracts):

D Pollux = 28° 01'.7 N = 28°.02833
SHA Pollux = 243° 41'.8 = 243°.69666

(the sidereal hour angle SHA is positive here, and D is negative)

D Vega   = 38° 47' N = 38°.78333
SHA Vega = 80° 47'.4 = 80°.79

Hourly variation of GHA γ: 15° 2'.5 = 15°.04166)

The sidereal hour angle SHA is measured from 0 to 360° in a westerly (clockwise) direction from the First Point of Aries.

The declination D is the angle between OA and the equatorial plane, and is measured from 0 to +90° towards the north and from 0 to -90° towards the south (comparable to latitude in the system of geographical co-ordinates).

Chapter 5

USING TRIGONOMETRY

THE TRIGONOMETRICAL CIRCLE AND BASIC EQUATIONS

Take a circle radius r = 1 (OA = 1) where B is a point on this circle (OB = 1). The circle is drawn in an anti-clockwise direction.

$$\sin a = \frac{\overline{OI}}{OB} = \overline{OI}$$

$$\cos a = \frac{\overline{OH}}{OB} = \overline{OH}$$

$$\text{tg } a = \frac{\overline{AT}}{OA} = \overline{AT}$$

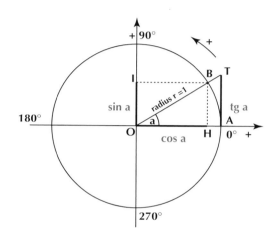

Notes

$\sin a = \sin (180° - a)$

$\cos a = \cos (360° - a)$

$\sin a = - \sin (- a)$

$\cos a = \cos (- a)$

$\cos (90° - a) = \sin a$

$\sin (90° - a) = \cos a$

$\sin (a + b) = \sin a \cos b + \sin b \cos a$

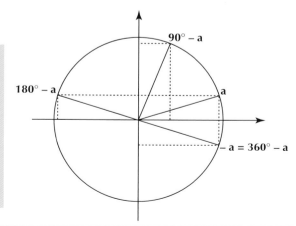

si $\sin a = \sin b$ then $a = b$ or $a = 180° - b$

si $\cos a = \cos b$ then $a = b$ or $a = 360° - b$

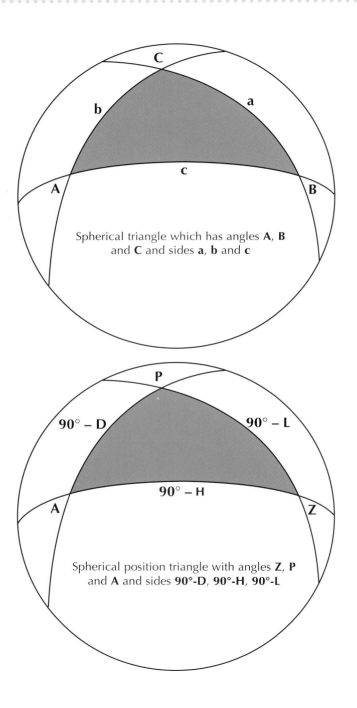

Spherical triangle which has angles **A**, **B** and **C** and sides **a**, **b** and **c**

Spherical position triangle with angles **Z**, **P** and **A** and sides **90°-D**, **90°-H**, **90°-L**

- Take a *sphere with a radius of 1.*
- Any circle whose plane passes through the centre of the sphere is a *great circle.*
- A *spherical triangle* is a figure formed by three arcs of great circles.
- The *arcs* are the sides of the triangle and are generally designated by lower case letters.

- The *angles of the spherical triangle* are in the corners where the arcs intersect. They are designated by upper case letters.
- If you join the triangle's corners to the centre of the sphere you create a trihedron whose dihedral angles are the angles of the triangle.

The co-ordinates are:

$$\overrightarrow{OB} \qquad \begin{aligned} X &= 0 \\ Y &= \sin c \\ Z &= \cos c \end{aligned} \qquad\qquad \overrightarrow{OC} \qquad \begin{aligned} X' &= \sin b \sin \text{angle } A \\ Y' &= \sin b \cos \text{angle } A \\ Z' &= \cos b \end{aligned}$$

Using two different ways of obtaining the scalar product:

$$\overline{OB}.\overline{OC} = \quad || \overrightarrow{OB} ||.\, || \overrightarrow{OC} || \cos a = 1 \times 1 \times \cos a = \cos a$$

$$XX' + YY' + ZZ' = \sin c \sin b \cos \text{angle } A + \cos c \cos b$$

From which we obtain the basic formula of spherical trigonometry:

$$\cos a = \cos b \cos c + \sin b \sin c \cos A$$

In other words
The length of the third side of a spherical triangle can always be determined if you know the other two sides and the angle they include.

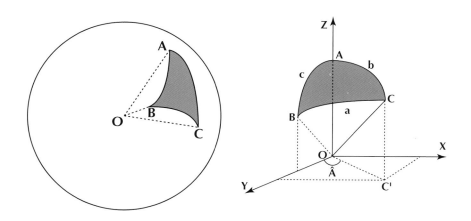

ON EARTH (TRIANGLE ZPA – ENGLISH METHOD)

In the spherical position triangle, we know that:
$\cos(90° - H) = \cos(90° - L) \cos(90° - D) + \sin(90° - L) \sin(90° - L) \cos(P)$.
Or $\cos(P) = \cos(LHA)$

> From which we obtain the basic equation:
> **$\sin Hc = \sin L \sin D + \cos L \cos D \cos LHA$**

In the triangle AZP of which the three sides and LHA are now known, we can deduce the internal angle Z by once more using the basic formula:

$\sin D = \sin Hc \sin L + \cos Hc \cos L \cos \text{angle } Z$, from which we derive:
$$\cos \text{angle } Z = \frac{\sin D - \sin L \sin Hc}{\cos L \cos Hc}$$

To find the calculated bearing Zc of the Sun:

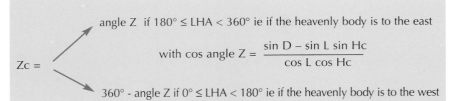

$Zc = $
angle Z if $180° \leq LHA < 360°$ ie if the heavenly body is to the east

with $\cos \text{angle } Z = \dfrac{\sin D - \sin L \sin Hc}{\cos L \cos Hc}$

$360°$ - angle Z if $0° \leq LHA < 180°$ ie if the heavenly body is to the west

So simply by calculation, without any observation, we have found the position of the Sun's Pg. To be more exact, we have used calculation to establish, at a given place and at a precise moment, two things:

1 The altitude and azimuth of the Sun
2 The distance between the Sun's Pg and the observer

(And of course anything said about the Sun applies equally to any other heavenly body)

IN SPACE (TRIANGLE ZPA – FRENCH METHOD)

Instead of working from the terrestrial sphere, we can apply exactly the same procedure to the celestial sphere. Since the two triangles ZPA, on Earth and in space, have the same shape, the basic formulae (given below) which determine their angles are identical.

Notes

1 When the Sun crosses the observer's meridian, the position triangle flattens into a single line. At this moment:

PA = PZ +/- ZA
  (+ if Z is between P and A;
  - if A is between P and Z)
90° - D = (90° - L) +/- (90° - H)

so **L = D +/- (90° - H) = D +/- ZD**

2 When LHA = 0, cos LHA = 1, and the basic equation becomes:

sin H = sin D sin L + cos L cos D or
sin H = sin D cos (90° - L) + sin (90° - L) cos D,
which is the same as sin (D + (90° - L)), therefore:
H = D (90° - L) or H = 180° - (D + 90° - L)

so **L = D +/- (90° - H) = D +/- ZD**

This is the formula to obtain latitude at the meridian.

▄▄▄ THE INTERNAL ANGLES P AND Z OF TRIANGLE ZPA FOR THE SUN ▄▄▄

Morning: the Sun is in the east. The calculated bearing Zc of the Sun = angle Z
LHA = external angle of triangle ZPA
Zc = angle Z = internal angle of triangle AZP

Since 180° < LHA, angle P = 360° - LHA

It is early morning on your foredeck; the local time is 0800h and LHA = 300°.

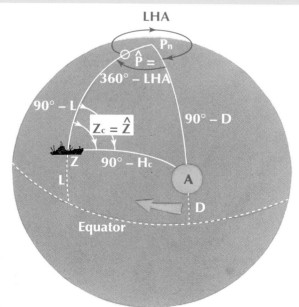

LHA

$\hat{P}$ =
360° – LHA

90° – L

90° – D

$Z_c = \hat{Z}$

Z   90° – Hc

L

A

D

Equator

Zc is the calculated bearing of the heavenly body.
The internal angle P of the triangle ZPA is called the *polar angle*.

LHA is the angle between the observer's meridian and that of the heavenly body.
Zc = Z is the internal angle of triangle AZP

Afternoon: the Sun is in the west.

The calculated bearing Zc of the Sun = 360° - angle Z

LHA = internal angle of triangle ZPA

Z is the internal angle, and Zc the external angle, of triangle AZP

Since LHA < 180°, angle P = LHA

Having passed the boat's meridian (midday), the Sun's position indicates that the local time is 1400h, and LHA= 30°.

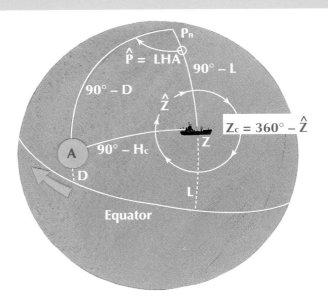

Notes

1 The angles are measured in a clockwise direction and, for LHA and Zc, from the observer's meridian towards the geographical position A = Pg of the heavenly body being observed.

2 Whether angle P = 360° - LHA or angle P = LHA, in every case: cos (angle P) = cos (LHA)

3 Do not confuse the calculated bearing or azimuth Zc we are dealing with here with a compass bearing in coastal navigation.

4 As an angular measurement, P is the shortest distance between the observer's meridian and the geographical position A = Pg of the heavenly body. The angle P is always less than 180°.

The observer's eye is assumed to be at the centre of the Earth. This simplification is acceptable because of the vast distances involved.

The world's axis $\overrightarrow{Ps - Pn}$ (which is aligned with the terrestrial poles) passes through its centre and is perpendicular to the celestial equator (in the same plane as the terrestrial equator).

The observer's horizon is perpendicular to the axis $\overrightarrow{Nadir - Zenith}$.

The heavenly body's vertical plane passes through:
- The centre of the earth (and the observer's eye)
- The zenith
- The heavenly body's position on the celestial sphere

The distance from the equator of the observer's zenith Z is the same as the latitude L, so that the arc PZ = 90° - L.

The heavenly body A's distance from the equator is its declination D, so that the arc PA = 90° - D.

The heavenly body A has an altitude H above the horizon, so that the arc ZA = 90° - H.

The famous spherical triangle has been formed. Its sides are:

- The arc PZ = 90° - L, which is called the colatitude;
- The arc PA = 90° - D, which is called the polar distance;
- The arc ZA = 90° - H, which is called the zenith distance.

The two triangles ZPA (in space and on the Earth) have the same shape.

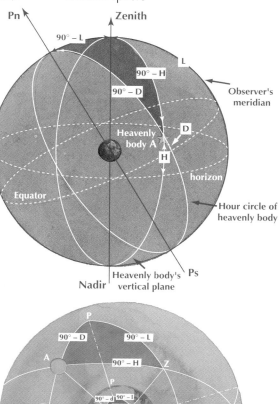

Chapter 6

THE ALTITUDE POSITION LINE

Preliminary geometrical construction

Take a position E, and from it mark off the position O at a distance Rc along the true azimuth or bearing Zv. E is known as the assumed position.

Taking O as the centre, draw a circle of radius Rc, which passes through E. From the same centre O draw a second circle of radius Rv.

Along the axis EO, the difference between the two radii is known as the *intercept I.*

I = Rv - Rc. In other words we have a vector, ie a line defining both distance and direction, passing through E. *The altitude position line* crosses it as a tangent of the circle Rv.

As well as the true bearing or azimuth Zv, the intercept vector represents the distance between two circles with a common centre.

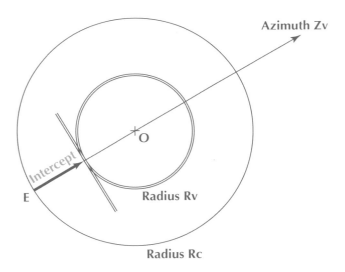

The altitude position line (shown with a double line) is perpendicular to the intercept.

Another, simpler and quicker approach, without drawing the two circles

Starting from a position E, draw a vector I = Rv - Rc along the azimuth Zv.

A perpendicular at the end of this is the altitude position line

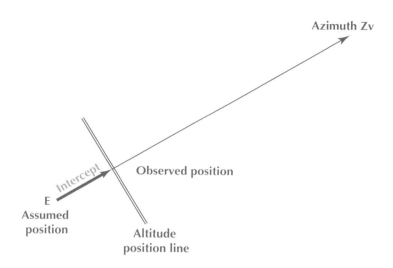

The observed position is at the intersection of the intercept and the altitude position line.

Assume you are at a position E on the chart not far from your estimated position (or you could take the estimated position itself as E). This position is known as the assumed position.

The distance from E to the Sun's Pg is 90° - Hc (calculated or tabulated altitude).

Now take a sextant sight Ho which puts you 90° - Ho from the Sun's Pg.

This gives us two measurements of our distance from the Sun's Pg: 90° - Hc and 90° - Ho.

The difference between these two distances is: (90° - Hc) - (90° - Ho) = Ho - Hc

So Ho - Hc measured in nautical miles is the *intercept*.

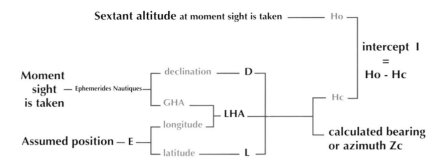

From the estimated position E on the chart, a line is drawn, orientated positively towards the Sun's footprint, along the calculated bearing or azimuth Zc.

Depending on the sign in front of I, the intercept takes the position line either towards or away from the Sun.

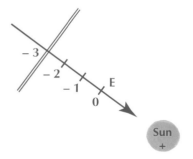

If Ho < Hc (ie Ho - Hc is negative), the intercept takes the position line away from the Sun.

I = -3 miles.

If Ho > Hc (ie Ho - Hc is positive), the intercept takes the position line towards the Sun.

I = + 2 miles.

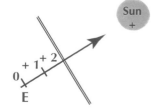

The perpendicular at the end of the intercept is the altitude position line, represented by a double line.

In practice, good observations are only possible under the following conditions:

• between latitudes - 60° and + 60°
• between altitudes 20° and 80°
• with an intercept < 30 miles

VARIOUS WAYS OF LOOKING AT THE ALTITUDE POSITION LINE

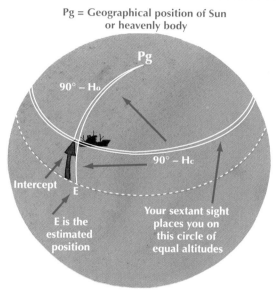

Pg = Geographical position of Sun
or heavenly body

Pg

90° – Ho

90° – Hc

Intercept

E

E is the
estimated
position

Your sextant sight
places you on
this circle of
equal altitudes

By now you will have probably realised two things:

1 The intercept is essentially a difference; since we cannot position ourselves directly by reference to Pg, we do it by establishing how far that position is from a known point E.

2 The choice of position E does not affect the altitude position line; in other words, position lines established (in the diagram below) from positions F, G, are identical with that established from E.

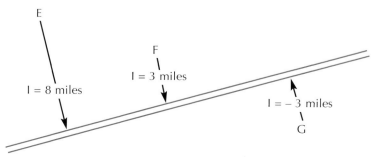

E

F

I = 3 miles

I = 8 miles

I = – 3 miles

G

47

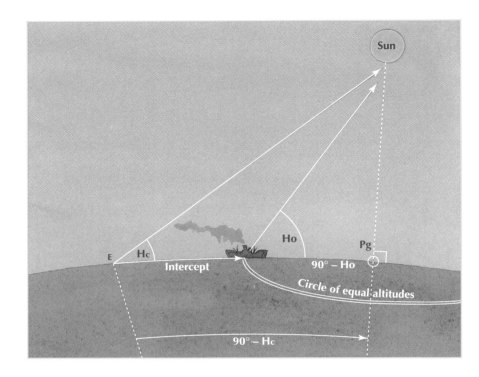

Position by bearings from two marks

With a hand bearing compass you can easily fix your position with two bearings.

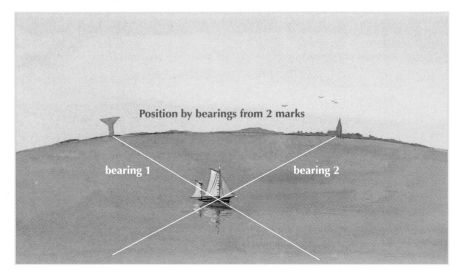

Position by bearings from 2 marks

Position by two altitude position lines from the Sun

Accurate to within five miles from position E.

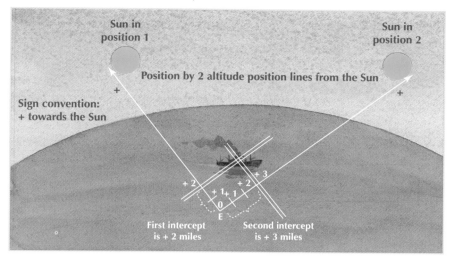

In the examples above and opposite, the observer is on a stationary boat.

If the boat is moving, the first bearing or position line will shift, depending on the vector V that defines its course and speed.

Chapter 7

THE MERIDIAN

Introduction

A particular type of position line is involved when the Sun is sighted at midday, local time, ie at the moment the Sun is on the boat's meridian. This method is difficult in cloudy conditions, and if the sight has to be retaken, you must wait 24 hours – a serious limitation.

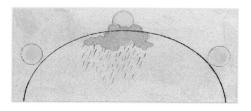

Ship in the northern hemisphere

Ship in the southern hemisphere

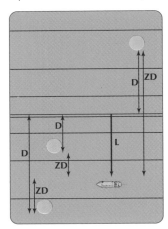

15° N

10° N

05° N

equator

05° S

10° S

15° S

Study the two diagrams above and you will see that the following relationship always holds good:

L = D +/- (90° - H)

+ if the sight is taken with the North Pole behind you

- if the sight is taken with the South Pole behind you

Example

On 30 August in the year N, in the northern hemisphere, we observe that the Sun reaches its highest point at 13h 42m 32s UT (= 13h.70888 UT in decimals). The sextant altitude Hs = 50° 36′ and the sight is taken with the North Pole behind us.

Hs	= 50 ° 36 ′
Index error correction	= 10′
Grouped corrections (height of eye 2m)	= 12′.8
Calendar correction	= - 00′.2
Ho	= 50° 58′.6

ZD = (90° - Ho) = 39°.02333

Latitude = D + ZD
        = 8°.85937 + 39°.02333
        = 47°.88270
        = 47° 52′.9

To calculate D on 30 August in the year N at 13h.70888 UT:

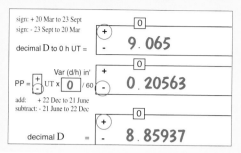

sign: + 20 Mar to 23 Sept
sign: - 23 Sept to 20 Mar

decimal D to 0 h UT =   (+/-)   [0]   - **9.065**

$$PP = \begin{matrix} + \\ - \end{matrix} \; UT \times \boxed{0} \; / 60 \; (+/-) \quad [0] \quad + \; \textbf{0.20563}$$

Var (d/h) in'

add: + 22 Dec to 21 June
subtract: - 21 June to 22 Dec

decimal D   =   (+/-)   [0]   - **8.85937**

LONGITUDE AT THE MERIDIAN

The Sun, in its hour circle, moving at an angular speed of 14°.999 an hour, crosses the Greenwich meridian on 23 May of the year N, at 11h 56m 43s UT. This is the famous T Pass (or Sun's meridian passage).

To make the calculations easier, we will round up the speed to 15° an hour. Only two hours later, ie at 13h 56m 43s UT, the Sun will be over our cargo vessel at 30° W.

Conversely, if I am on a boat, not knowing my longitude but with access to a watch keeping UT, I simply have to note the exact moment (to the nearest second) when the Sun reaches its highest point and crosses my meridian.

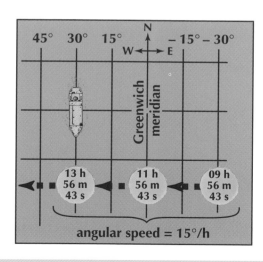

The time difference multiplied by the speed gives us the longitude:
Longitude G = (t - T Pass) x 15°/h

In practice, the Sun's altitude barely changes for at least a minute as it crosses the meridian, which makes it difficult to establish the precise moment t when it reaches its highest point.

So half an hour before it arrives, take a first sight H, at the time t1, and then take a second sight half an hour afterwards, without adjusting the sextant, and note the time as t2.

Because of this symmetry, the Sun reaches its highest point at (t1 + t2)/2. In fact you can take any number of sights and work out the average time; if there are four, the highest point will be at (t1 + t2 + t3 + t4)/4.

Example 1

On 23 May in the year N, the T Pass = 11h 56m 43s and we record that t1 = 10h 20m 13s, and t2 = 11h 17m 56s.

t = (t1 + t2)/2 = 10h.81791
t - T Pass   = -1h.12736
Longitude = (t-T Pass) x 15°/h = -16° 54'.37, ie 16° 54'.6 E, under the boot of Italy.

Example 2

On the same 23 May, T Pass = 11h 56m 43s and we record that t1 = 16h 18m 10s and t2 = 17h 00m 05s.

t = (t1 + t2)/2 = 16h.65208
t - T Pass   = 4h.70680
Longitude = (t-T Pass) x 15°/h = 70° 36'.72, which puts us at 70° 36'.1 W off Santo Domingo.

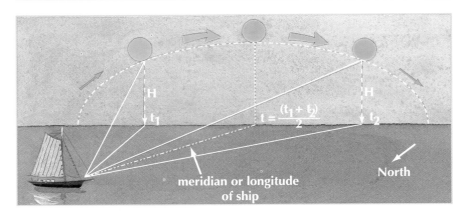

Notes

1 Calculations can be greatly simplified, as suggested earlier, by using a pocket calculator to convert sexagesimals automatically into decimals.

2 The formula used here is related to the definition of speed: v = distance/time, a formula that can equally be expressed as: distance = time x speed, or as: difference in longitude = elapsed time x 15°/h.

A COMPLETE EXAMPLE OF LONGITUDE AT THE MERIDIAN

On Thursday 9 July in the year N+1, imagine that we are in the open sea equipped with a sextant, a watch perfectly adjusted to UT, and the relevant section of the almanac:

T Pass = 12h 05m 11s.

At around midday, local time, we watch the Sun climb, reach a plateau, and then begin to descend.

We take ten sights (five as the Sun is rising, A to E, and five as it descends, A' to E').

The raw, uncorrected data is recorded in the following tables:

Total time of observation: 1h 30m

Sun rising	Time UT
A	11 h 02 m 16 s
B	11 h 07 m 31 s
C	11 h 16 m 31 s
D	11 h 25 m 32 s
E	11 h 32 m 30 s

Sextant altitude Hs
67° 29′. 0
67° 52′. 6
68° 23′. 4
68° 45′. 2
68° 55′. 4

Sun descending	Time UT
A′	12 h 20 m 45 s
B′	12 h 15 m 13 s
C′	12 h 06 m 08 s
D′	11 h 56 m 52 s
E′	11 h 50 m 39 s

In decimals, the data becomes:

Sun rising	Time UT
A	11 h. 03777
B	11 h. 12527
C	11 h. 27527
D	11 h. 42555
E	11 h. 54166

Sextant altitude Hs
67°. 48333
67°. 87666
68°. 39000
68°. 75333
68°. 92333

Sun descending	Time UT
A′	12 h. 34583
B′	12 h. 25361
C′	12 h. 10222
D′	11 h. 94777
E′	11 h. 84416

It is always worthwhile visualising the series of sights diagrammatically.

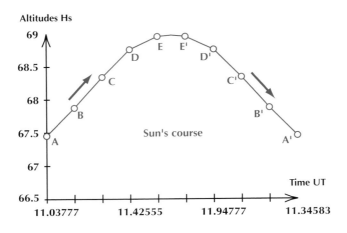

Notes

It is not possible simply to record time and altitude when the Sun is at its highest. You can estimate them by drawing a smooth curve with a pencil, joining the sights, but this is not very accurate.

Finding your longitude (using three different sets of figures)

Using tA and tA'
> **longitude G** = [(tA + tA')/2 - T Pass]   x 15°/h
>   = (11h.69180 - 12h 05m 11s)   x 15 °/h = **-5° 55'.13**

Using tB and tB'
> **longitude G** = [(tB + tB')/2 - T Pass]   x 15 °/h
>   = (11h.68944 - 12h 05m 11s)   x 15 °/h = **- 5° 57'.25**

Using tA, tB, tA' and tB'
> **longitude G** = [(tA + tB + tA' + tB')/4 - T Pass]   x 15°/h
>   = (11h.69062 - 12h 05m 11s)   x 15°/h = **5° 56'.19**

You could equally well do the calculation using C and C', D and D', E and E'. If you use all ten sights A,B,C,D,E, and A',B',C',D',E', the longitude G = 5° 56'.83.

GPS shows the longitude as 5° 55'.9 E, which is very close.

■■■■■ NOTES ON OBTAINING THE LONGITUDE BY THIS METHOD ■■■■■

1 Taking a series of sights from the bridge deck of a small sailing vessel is a tricky business. It is certainly not a particularly accurate method, and requires a lot of care – some authors ignore it altogether.

2 Theoretically it is assumed that the boat barely moves in a north-south direction between the Sun sights $H1$ and $H2$. However if the movement is significant (for example a catamaran going at 15 knots might move 13 miles north-south, which is 13 minutes of latitude), it is possible to take account of it by adjusting the first sight $H1$ (which becomes $H'1$) by the amount of north-south movement expressed in minutes of latitude. So if $H1 = 38°\ 11'$, and if the boat is heading towards the Sun, stop the catamaran after an hour and record the time t2 where H2 = $H'1$ = $38°\ 11' + 13' = 38°\ 24$minutes.

Southerly movement

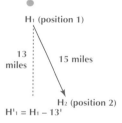

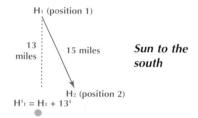

Northerly movement

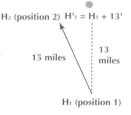

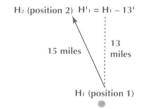

From this, it follows that, taking north-south movement into account:

$$H'1 = H1 +/- \text{ change in latitude}$$

$+$

If movement is towards Sun's geographical position Pg

$-$

If movement is away from Sun's geographical position Pg

55

On Friday 17 April in the year N+1, a sight is taken from a height of 2 metres, showing that the Sun reaches an altitude of 57° 08'.8, at precisely 11h 37 m 09s UT.

The declination of the Sun D = 10° 19'.5 N at 0h UT, and its hourly variation is 0'.9/h.

Working out the latitude

When the Sun is at its highest, its altitude above the horizon is measured:

Hs	=	57° 08'.8	
Index error correction	=	0'	
Grouped corrections	=	+ 12'.9	
Calendar correction	=	0'	
Ho	=	57° 21'.7	= 57°.36166
ZD	=	90° - 57°.36166	= 32°.63833

Value of D when the Sun reaches its highest point, ie at 11h 37m 09s = 11h.61916

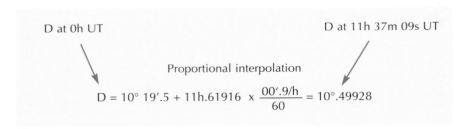

D at 0h UT

D at 11h 37m 09s UT

Proportional interpolation

$$D = 10° 19'.5 + 11h.61916 \times \frac{00'.9/h}{60} = 10°.49928$$

Since the sight was taken with the north pole at our back: L = D + ZD = 43°.13761

= 43°08'.26

GPS showed the latitude as 43° 04'.38 N, giving a difference of 3.88 miles.

Chapter 8

CALCULATION FORMATS

Depending on the nature of the calculation, there are two prepared formats you can use:

GRAPHIC

A format providing for a series of five Sun sights that can be recorded on a graph.

NON-GRAPHIC

A matrix equally suitable for observations of the Sun, the planets or the stars (one sight at a time).

Example

Altitude position line from a single Sun sight, taken at an estimated position:

- L = 49° 10'.02 N
- G = 03° 49'.98 W
- From a height of 2 metres.

The altitude reading at the Sun's edge Hs = 19° 13'.45.
The days are lengthening; the Sun is below the equator.

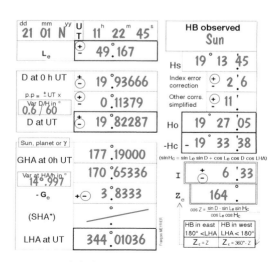

HB = Heavenly body

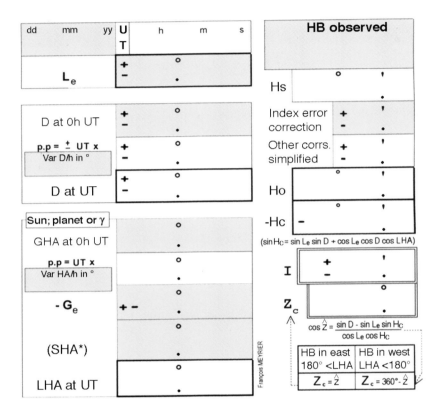

The boxes coloured blue can be filled in before taking the sight.

CONVERTING SEXAGESIMALS INTO DECIMALS

On a Casio FX-115MS calculator, use this key

Example 1 To obtain the decimal value of 16 h 19 m 43 s

16 [° , ,,]   19 [° , ,,]   43 [° , ,,]   and it shows 16.3286

Example 2 To obtain the decimal value of 2° 22'.73

2 [° , ,,]   22.73 [° , ,,]   and it shows 2° 2.37883

Conversely, the save key can be used to change decimal values into sexagesimals.

Example To convert 10.50 hours into decimals,

use the sequence 10.50 [° , ,,]   and it shows 10° 30° 0

which represents ten hours thirty minutes in sexagesimals.

Note
In the following series of exercises, the sights are taken with a variety of sextants, so the index errors (and therefore their corrections) also vary.

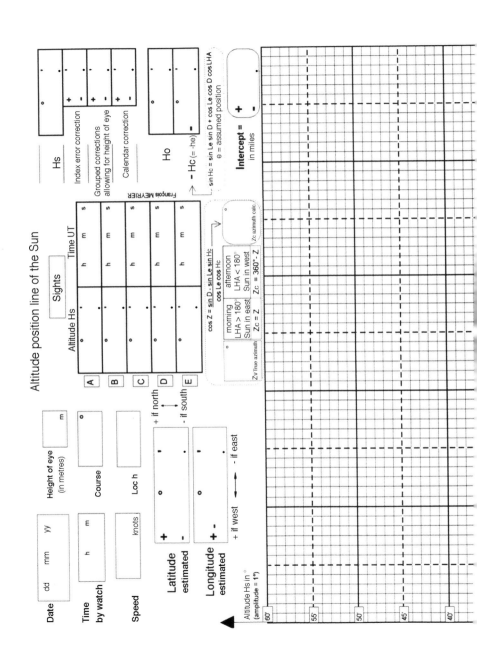

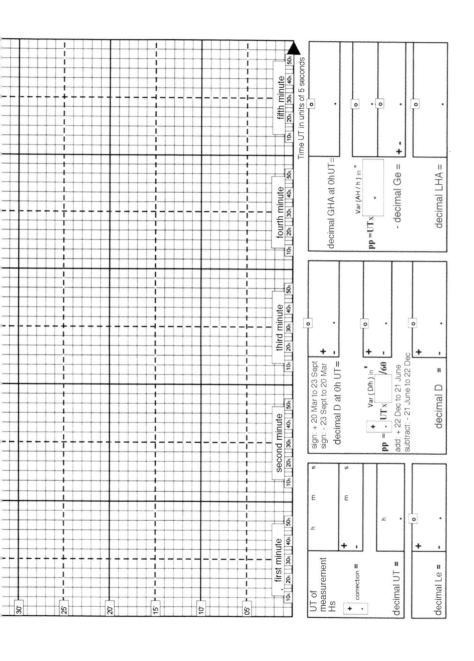

Chapter 9

PROBLEMS AND ANSWERS

USING A PRINTED FORMAT

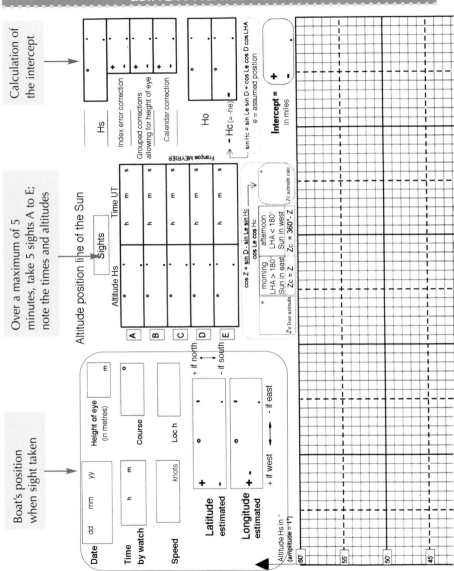

Boat's position when sight taken

| Date | dd | mm | yy |

| Time by watch | h | m | |

Height of eye (in metres): m

Course: °

Speed: knots

Loc h:

Latitude estimated + if north − if south

Longitude estimated + if west − if east

Altitude Hs in ° (amplitude = 1°)

Altitude position line of the Sun

Over a maximum of 5 minutes, take 5 sights A to E; note the times and altitudes

Sights

	Altitude Hs °	Time UT h m s
A		
B		
C		
D		
E		

$$\cos Z = \frac{\sin D - \sin Le \sin Hc}{\cos Le \cos Hc}$$

morning — LHA > 180° — Sun in east — Zc = Z

afternoon — LHA < 180° — Sun in west — Zc = 360° − Z

Zv true azimuth — Zc azimuth calc.

Calculation of the intercept

Hs

Index error correction

Grouped corrections allowing for height of eye

Calendar correction

François MEYRIER

Ho

− Hc (= -he)

$\sin Hc = \sin Le \sin D + \cos Le \cos D \cos LHA$

e = assumed position

Intercept = in miles

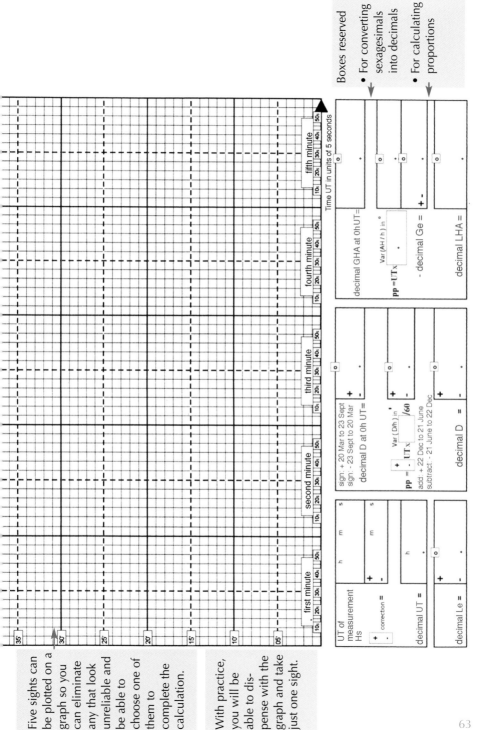

Five sights can be plotted on a graph so you can eliminate any that look unreliable and be able to choose one of them to complete the calculation.

With practice, you will be able to dispense with the graph and take just one sight.

Boxes reserved
• For converting sexagesimals into decimals
• For calculating proportions

Time UT in units of 5 seconds

first minute | second minute | third minute | fourth minute | fifth minute

decimal GHA at 0h UT =

$pp = UT_x \cdot \dfrac{Var\,(AH/h)\ in\ °}{}$

− decimal Ge =

decimal LHA =

sign: + 20 Mar to 23 Sept
sign: − 23 Sept to 20 Mar

decimal D at 0h UT =

$pp = UT_x \cdot \dfrac{Var\,(D/h)\ in\ '}{60}$

add: + 22 Dec to 21 June
subtract: − 21 June to 22 Dec

decimal D =

UT of measurement
Hs
correction =

decimal UT =

decimal Le =

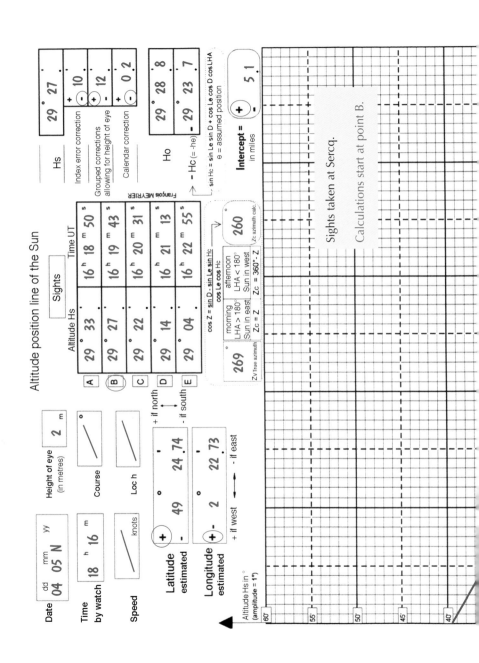

Altitude position line of the Sun

Date 04 (dd) 05 N (mm yy)

Height of eye (in metres) 2 m

Time by watch 18 h 16 m

Course

Speed knots

Loc h

Latitude estimated (+/−) 49° 24.74 · + if north — if south

Longitude estimated (+/−) 2° 22.73 · + if west — if east

Altitude Hs in ° (amplitude = 1°)

Sights

	Altitude Hs	Time UT
A	29° 33 ·	16 h 18 m 50 s
B	29° 27 ·	16 h 19 m 43 s
C	29° 22 ·	16 h 20 m 31 s
D	29° 14 ·	16 h 21 m 13 s
E	29° 04 ·	16 h 22 m 55 s

François MEYRIER

$\cos Z = \dfrac{\sin D - \sin Le \sin Hc}{\cos Le \cos Hc}$

morning	afternoon
LHA > 180°	LHA < 180°
Sun in east	Sun in west
Zc = Z	Zc = 360° - Z

269° Zv true azimuth → 260° Zc azimuth calc.

Hs 29° 27 ·

Index error correction + (·) − 10
Grouped corrections allowing for height of eye + (·) − 12
Calendar correction + (·) − 0 2

$\sin Hc = \sin Le \sin D + \cos Le \cos D \cos LHA$

e = assumed position

Ho 29° 28 · 8
→ − Hc (= −he) − 29° 23 · 7

Intercept = (+/−) 5 · 1 in miles

Sights taken at Sercq.

Calculations start at point B.

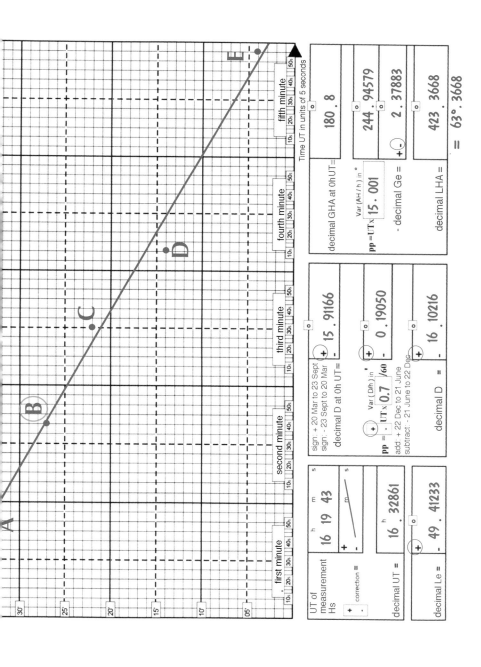

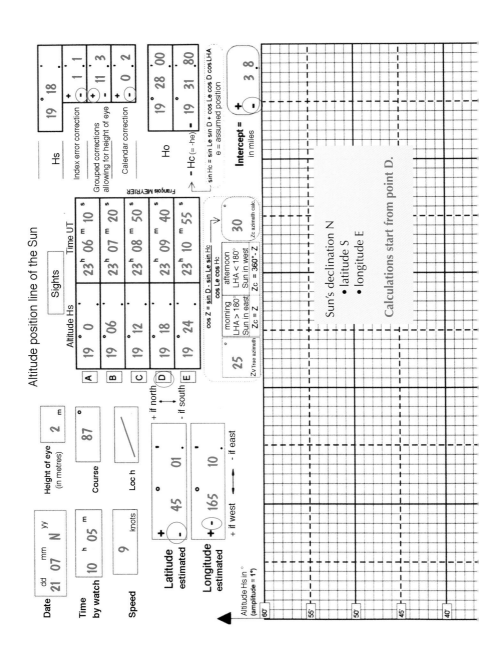

Altitude position line of the Sun

Date: dd 21 | mm 07 | yy N

Height of eye (in metres): 2 m

Time by watch: 10 h 05 m

Course: 87 °

Speed: 9 knots

Loc h

Latitude estimated: + - | 45 ° 01 . | + if north ↔ - if south

Longitude estimated: + - | 165 ° 10 . | + if east ↔ - if west

Altitude Hs in ° (amplitude = 1°)

Sights

	Altitude Hs	Time UT
A	19 ° 0 .	23 h 06 m 10 s
B	19 ° 06 .	23 h 07 m 20 s
C	19 ° 12 .	23 h 08 m 50 s
D	19 ° 18 .	23 h 09 m 40 s
E	19 ° 24 .	23 h 10 m 55 s

François MEYRIER

cos Z = sin D - sin Le sin Hc / cos Le cos Hc

	morning	afternoon
	LHA > 180°	LHA < 180°
	Sun in east	Sun in west
	Zc = Z	Zc = 360°- Z

25 ° Zv True azimuth   30 ° Zc azimuth calc.

Hs: 19 ° 18 .

Index error correction: + - | 1 . 1
Grouped corrections allowing for height of eye: + - | 11 . 3
Calendar correction: + - | 0 . 2

Ho: 19 ° 28 . 00

sin Hc = sin Le sin D + cos Le cos D cos LHA
e = assumed position

- Hc (= -he): - 19 ° 31 . 80

Intercept = in miles: + - | 3 . 8

Sun's declination N
• latitude S
• longitude E

Calculations start from point D.

60'
55'
50'
45'
40'

66

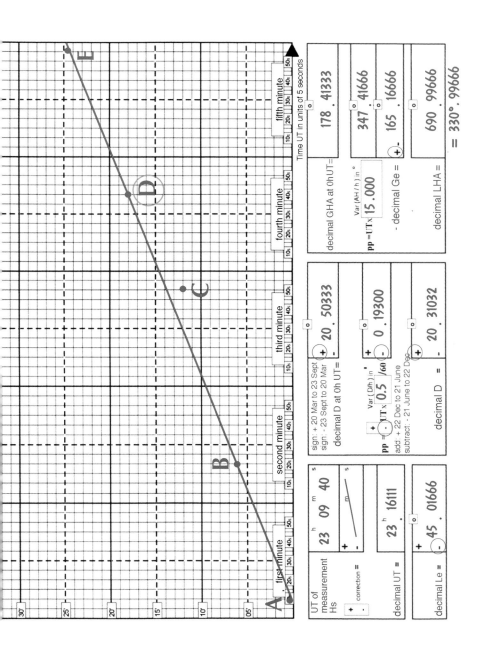

The graph axis labels: 30', 25', 20', 15', 10', 05'

Points: A, B, C, D, E

first minute | second minute | third minute | fourth minute | fifth minute

Time UT in units of 5 seconds

10⎖ 20⎖ 30⎖ 40⎖ 50⎖ (repeated per minute)

UT of measurement
Hs

23 ʰ 09 ᵐ 40 ˢ

+ ⊖ correction = ____ ᵐ ____ ˢ

decimal UT = 23 ʰ . 16111

decimal Le = ⊕ ⊖ 45 . 01666

sign: + 20 Mar to 23 Sept
sign: − 23 Sept to 20 Mar

decimal D at 0h UT = ⊕ − 20 . 50333

$pp = \frac{Var\,(D/h)\,in}{x\,0.5}$ UT x 0.5 /60   ⊕ − + . 19300

add: + 22 Dec to 21 June
subtract: − 21 June to 22 Dec

decimal D = ⊕ − 20 . 31032

decimal GHA at 0hUT = 178 . 41333 °

$pp = $ Var(AH/h) in ° UT x 15.000   347 . 41666 °

− decimal Ge = ⊕ − 165 . 16666 °

decimal LHA = 690 . 99666 °

= 330° . 99666

Altitude position line of the Sun

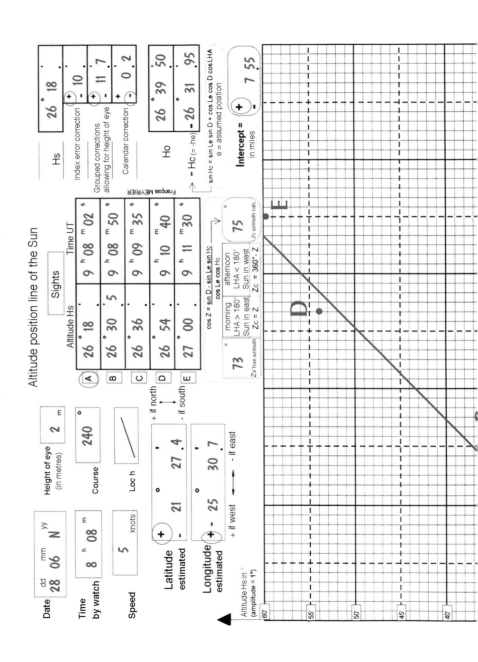

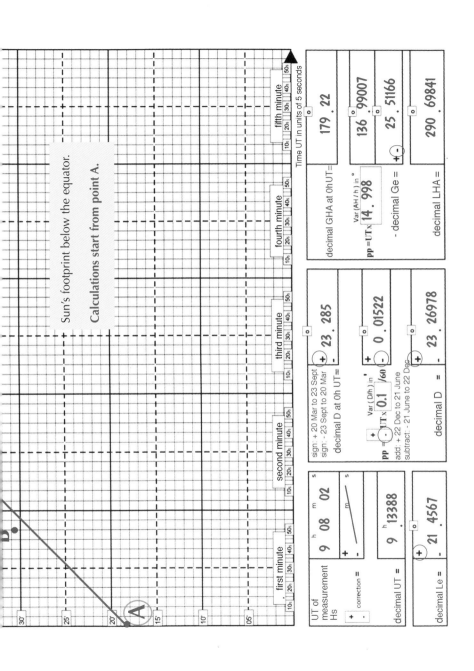

Sun's footprint below the equator.

Calculations start from point A.

Time UT in units of 5 seconds

first minute | second minute | third minute | fourth minute | fifth minute

UT of measurement Hs
+ − | 9ʰ 08ᵐ 02ˢ
correction = + − ᵐ ˢ

decimal UT = 9ʰ . 13388

decimal Le = + − | 21 . 4567 °

sign: + 20 Mar to 23 Sept
sign: − 23 Sept to 20 Mar
decimal D at 0h UT= + − | 23 . 285 °

pp = − UTx $\frac{Var(D/h) in '}{60}$ 0.1 ' + − | 0 . 01522 °

add: + 22 Dec to 21 June
subtract: − 21 June to 22 Dec
decimal D = + − | 23 . 26978 °

decimal GHA at 0hUT= | 179 . 22 °

pp = UTx Var(AH/h) in ° 14 . 998 | 136 . 99007 °

− decimal Ge = + − | 25 . 5166 °

decimal LHA = | 290 . 69841 °

Altitude position line of the Sun

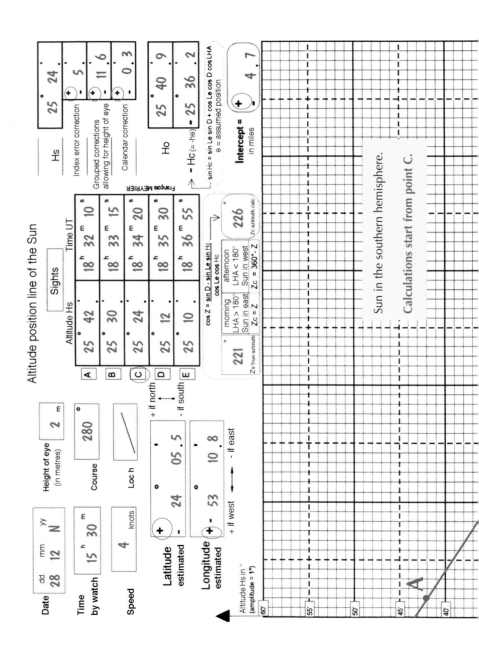

Sights

	Altitude Hs	Time UT
A	25° 42.'	18h 32m 10s
B	25° 30.'	18h 33m 15s
C	25° 24.'	18h 34m 20s
D	25° 12.'	18h 35m 30s
E	25° 10.'	18h 36m 55s

François MEYRIER

Date dd 28 | mm 12 | yy N

Time by watch 15h 30m

Speed 4 knots

Height of eye (in metres) 2 m

Course 280°

Loc h

+ if north ←→ - if south

Latitude estimated − 24° 05.5'

Longitude estimated + − 53° 10.8'

+ if west ←→ - if east

Altitude Hs in ° (amplitude = 1°)

60'
55'
50'
45'
40'

Hs 25° 24.'

Index error correction (+ −) 5.

Grouped corrections allowing for height of eye (+ −) 11.6

Calendar correction (+ −) 0.3

Ho 25° 40.'9

− Hc (= −he) − 25° 36.2

$\sin Hc = \sin Le \sin D + \cos Le \cos D \cos LHA$

he = assumed position

Intercept = in miles (+ −) 4.7

$\cos Z = \dfrac{\sin D - \sin Le \sin Hc}{\cos Le \cos Hc}$

	morning LHA > 180° Sun in east	afternoon LHA < 180° Sun in west
	Zc = Z	Zc = 360° - Z

Zc azimuth calc. 226

Zv True azimuth 221°

Sun in the southern hemisphere.

Calculations start from point C.

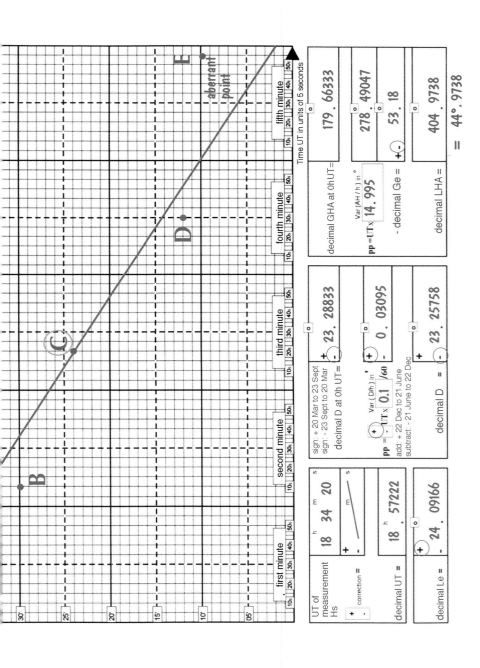

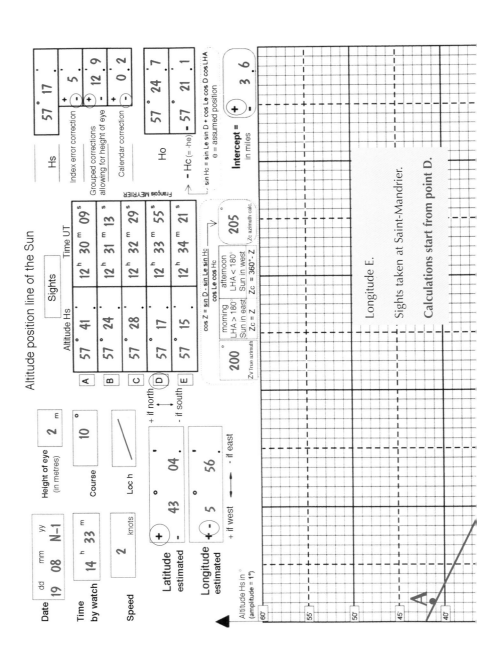

Altitude position line of the Sun

Date | dd 19 | mm 08 | yy N-1

Time by watch 14 h 33 m

Speed 2 knots

Height of eye (in metres) 2 m

Course 10 °

Loc h

Latitude estimated (+) - 43 ° 04 . ' + if north ← → - if south

Longitude estimated (+ -) 5 ° 56 . ' + if west — - if east

Altitude Hs in °
(amplitude = 1°)

Sights	Altitude Hs	Time UT
A	57 ° 41 . '	12 h 30 m 09 s
B	57 ° 24 . '	12 h 31 m 13 s
C	57 ° 28 . '	12 h 32 m 29 s
D	57 ° 17 . '	12 h 33 m 55 s
E	57 ° 15 . '	12 h 34 m 21 s

François MEYRIER

Hs 57 ° 17 . '

Index error correction (-) (+) + 5 .

Grouped corrections allowing for height of eye (-) 12 . 9

Calendar correction (+) (-) 0 . 2

Ho 57 ° 24 . 7

- Hc (= -he) - 57 ° 21 . 1

sin Hc = sin Le sin D + cos Le cos D cosLHA
e = assumed position

Intercept = (+) - 3 . 6
in miles

$$\cos Z = \frac{\sin D - \sin Le \sin Hc}{\cos Le \cos Hc}$$

	morning	afternoon
	LHA > 180°	LHA < 180°
	Sun in east	Sun in west
Zv True azimuth 200	Zc = Z	Zc = 360° - Z

→ 205 Zc azimuth calc.

Longitude E.

Sights taken at Saint-Mandrier.

Calculations start from point D.

60 55 50 45 40

A

72

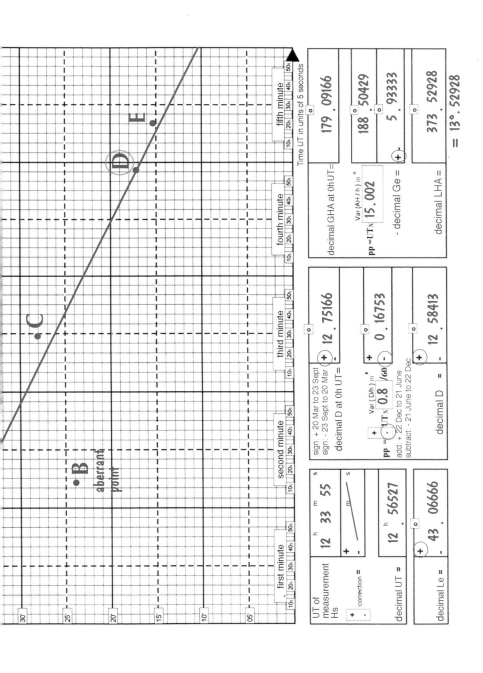

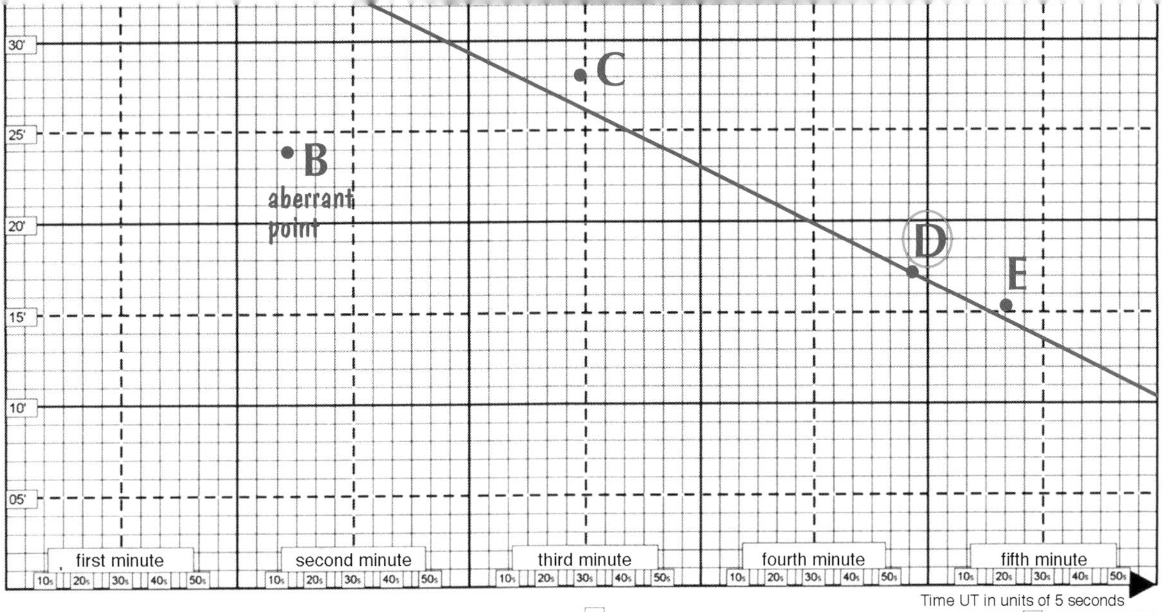
30'
25'
20'
15'
10'
05'
C
B
aberrant point
D
E
first minute
second minute
third minute
fourth minute
fifth minute
10s 20s 30s 40s 50s
Time UT in units of 5 seconds

UT of measurement Hs	12 h 33 m 55 s
correction = (+ / -)	+ / - (crossed out) m s
decimal UT =	12 h. 56527
decimal Le =	(+) 43°. 06666

sign: + 20 Mar to 23 Sept sign: - 23 Sept to 20 Mar decimal D at 0h UT=	(+) 12°. 75166
pp = (-) UT x Var (D/h) in ' 0.8 /60 add: + 22 Dec to 21 June subtract: - 21 June to 22 Dec	(-) 0°. 16753
decimal D =	(+) 12°. 58413

decimal GHA at 0h UT=	179°. 09166
pp = UT x Var (AH / h) in ° 15.002	188°. 50429
- decimal Ge =	(+) 5°. 93333
decimal LHA =	373°. 52928
	= 13°. 52928

Chapter 10

STAR POSITIONS

Star sights pose particular problems:

1 You cannot begin to fix your position from star sights until you can confidently recognise the main first magnitude stars – and that requires some training.

2 You can only take a sextant sight when the horizon is clearly visible, which means for a quarter of an hour at most, at dawn and dusk.

3 Watch out for a blurred horizon, especially if there are mist patches on the sea.

4 As night falls, or daylight approaches, you must quickly identify two or three stars whose hour circles are separated by an angle of 30° or more.

5 Two star sights whose bearings are 90° apart will produce position lines intersecting at right angles, therefore providing a very clear fix.

6 Even better, a sextant position using three stars will put you in the centre of a triangle formed by the three position lines.

7 With star fixes you do not transfer position lines because you are using two, or even three, celestial marks.

8 By holding the sextant upside down, instead of dropping the star on to the horizon (at the risk of losing it among all the other stars), you can lift the horizon (there is only one of these) to the star, a much simpler procedure.

9 Good sights can be obtained with a telescope that has no lenses; a simple tube with a central aperture is all you need.

10 The calculations are exactly the same as for the Sun, except for the following differences: stars have no apparent diameter; you use the hour angle of the First Point of Aries (instead of the Sun) which changes at a constant rate: Var/h GHAγ = 15° 2'.5 = 15°.04166; the local hour angle:

$$\text{LHA*} = \text{GHA}\gamma - \text{G} + \text{SHA*}$$

11 There is obviously not enough time to take several sights of each star and plot them on a graph – one sight per star, not more.

12 And finally, a personal view: there is something magical about fixing your position by the stars; it combines the principle of the altitude position line with a knowledge of the night sky.

On a clear night at sea, there are more than 2,000 stars visible to the naked eye. To recognise all of them is practically impossible, and of no use anyway.

For navigational purposes, the *Ephémérides Nautiques* provide the celestial co-ordinates of 81 of them, which is generally sufficient.

For the purposes of this book, we shall limit ourselves to the following 16 stars: Castor, Pollux, Capella (the goat), Procyon, Sirius, Fomalhaut, Arcturus, Spica, Antares, Regulus, Betelgeuse, Rigel, Cassiopeia, Altair, Deneb and Vega.

These stars, easily spotted from a boat, are said to be of the first magnitude, which means they are the brightest visible in the northern hemisphere.

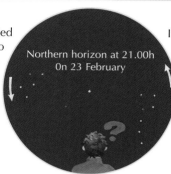

Northern horizon at 21.00h
On 23 February

If you face north and look at the night sky (as in the illustration opposite), you can observe the diurnal rhythm, or movement of the celestial vault in the direction shown by the arrows.

The first constellation (group of stars) to find is the Great Bear (also known as the Plough), which is always visible whatever the time of year. Its characteristic shape makes it easy to identify (see illustration at the top of next page). If you extend the line joining Merak and Dubhe for five times that distance, it leads to the Pole Star. Unfortunately for us, the Pole Star is not situated exactly at the celestial north pole, but less than a degree separates the two.

So, to within less than a degree, the altitude of the Pole Star is equal to the observer's latitude (see diagram at bottom of next page).

The following illustrations show sections of the night sky where the 16 first magnitude stars will be found (see pages 76-80).

Northern horizon at 03.00h
on 24 February

Finally, a sketch map of the night sky is shown on which to practise finding the stars. The correct identification is shown in the illustration on page 82.

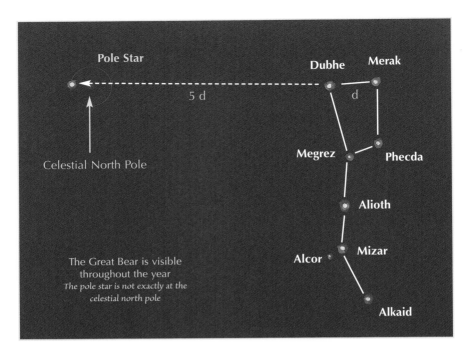

Pole Star

Dubhe   **Merak**

5 d   d

Celestial North Pole

Megrez

Phecda

Alioth

Alcor   **Mizar**

The Great Bear is visible
throughout the year
*The pole star is not exactly at the
celestial north pole*

Alkaid

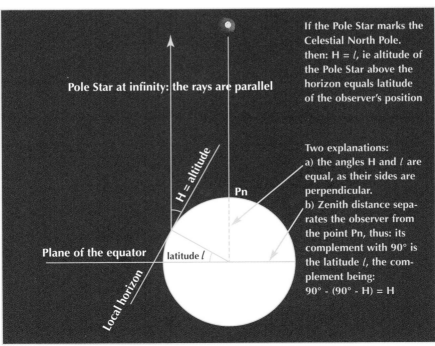

Pole Star at infinity: the rays are parallel

H = altitude

Pn

Plane of the equator   latitude *l*

Local horizon

If the Pole Star marks the
Celestial North Pole.
then: H = *l*, ie altitude of
the Pole Star above the
horizon equals latitude
of the observer's position

Two explanations:
a) the angles H and *l* are
equal, as their sides are
perpendicular.
b) Zenith distance sepa-
rates the observer from
the point Pn, thus: its
complement with 90° is
the latitude *l*, the complement being:
90° - (90° - H) = H

76

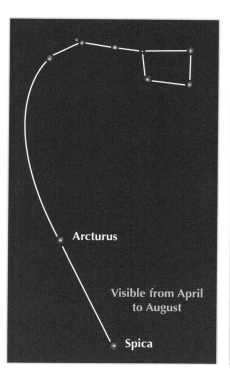

Arcturus

Visible from April to August

Spica

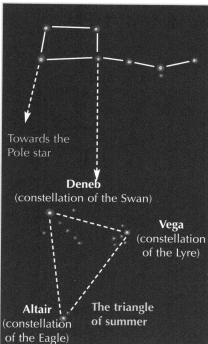

Towards the Pole star

Deneb
(constellation of the Swan)

Vega
(constellation of the Lyre)

Altair
(constellation of the Eagle)

The triangle of summer

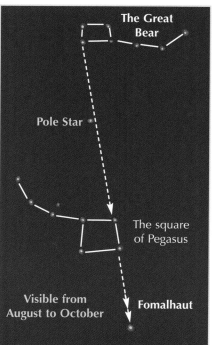

The Great Bear

Pole Star

The square of Pegasus

Visible from August to October

Fomalhaut

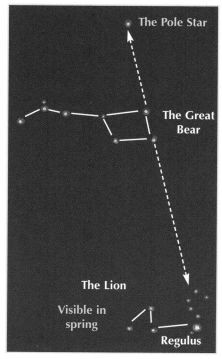

The Pole Star

The Great Bear

The Lion

Visible in spring

Regulus

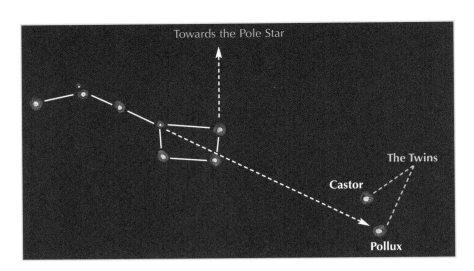

Towards the Pole Star

The Twins

Castor

Pollux

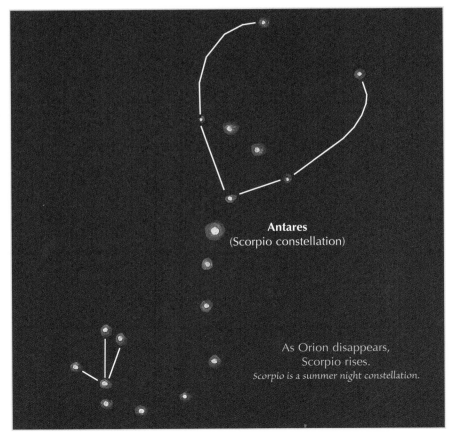

Antares
(Scorpio constellation)

As Orion disappears,
Scorpio rises.
Scorpio is a summer night constellation.

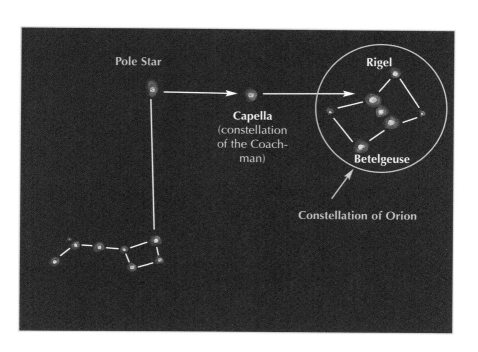

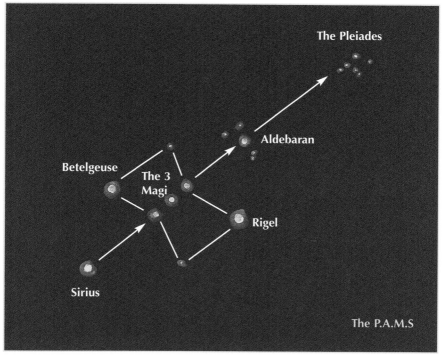

The P.A.M.S

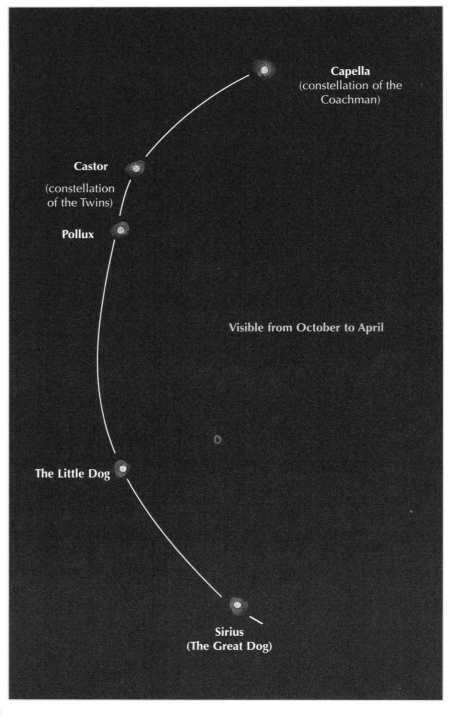

Capella
(constellation of the
Coachman)

Castor

(constellation
of the Twins)

Pollux

Visible from October to April

The Little Dog

Sirius
(The Great Dog)

Here is a small exercise in recognising the 16 first magnitude stars. Imagine a sky like this – either at the beginning of the evening or the end of the night.

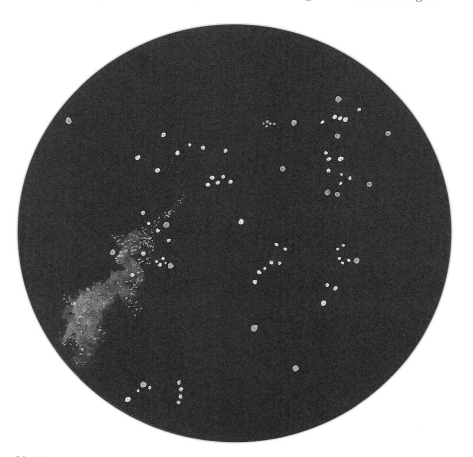

Notes

1 For the sake of simplicity, this map of the sky contains only a very limited number of stars, including the 16 first magnitude stars you need to recognise. Some intermediate ones are shown to help establish the alignments shown in the preceding illustrations.

2 In reality, you will never see a sky like this. The stars are not all visible at once; some rise as others set. Only the stars around the pole are visible all the year round.

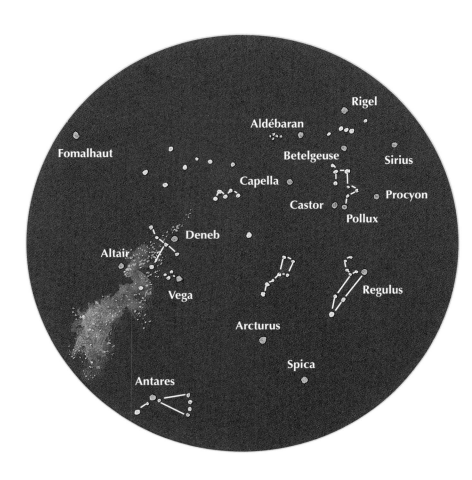

Rigel
Aldébaran
Fomalhaut
Betelgeuse
Sirius
Capella
Castor
Procyon
Pollux
Deneb
Altair
Vega
Regulus
Arcturus
Spica
Antares

WHEN ARE STARS VISIBLE?

The visibility of a star X with a declination D depends on the observer's latitude L, in accordance with the following rule (only applicable in the northern hemisphere; in the southern hemisphere the rule is reversed):

$(90° - L) < D$	Visible all night (the polar stars)
$-(90° - L) < D$, $(90° - L)$	Visible for a certain time (stars which rise and set)
$D < -(90° - L)$	Invisible all night

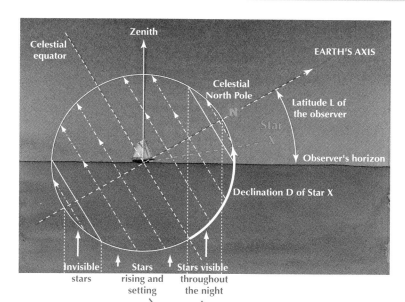

Zenith
Celestial equator
EARTH'S AXIS
Celestial North Pole
Latitude L of the observer
N
Star X
Observer's horizon
Declination D of Star X

Invisible stars | Stars rising and setting | Stars visible throughout the night

Example

From Paris, where L = 49° and (90° - L) = 41°.

Capella the goat (D = 46°) and Deneb (D = -45°) are always visible since 41° < 46° and 41° < 45°.

Arcturus (D = 19°) and Pollux (D = 28°) rise and set since -41° < 19° < 41° and -41° < 28° < 41°.

Canopus (D = -52°) and Archenar (D = -57°) are totally invisible since -52° < -41° and -57° < -41°.

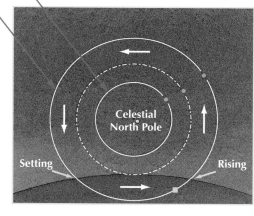

Celestial North Pole
Setting
Rising

● = visible star   ▨ = invisible star

INTERSECTION OF POSITION LINES · TRANSFERRED LINES · PLOTTING SHEETS FOR MERCATOR CHARTS

FIXING A POSITION BY THE INTERSECTION OF TWO TRANSFERRED POSITION LINES

Remember we are trying to establish our precise position on the chart, as defined by its longitude and latitude. But drawing just one altitude position line is not sufficient, because although this places us geometrically, it does not indicate a unique position. For that, we need a second position line derived from a second sextant sight.

WHEN THE BOAT IS STATIONARY

We are at anchor (position E) in the Baie de Cavalas south of the Saint Mandrier peninsula. By taking coastal bearings we have fixed our position precisely at 43° 04'.3 N, 5° 55'.9 E.

The aim is to find that position again using two measurements of the Sun's altitude. The two measurements are taken at an interval of four hours (from a height of 2 metres). For the position lines to produce a clear fix, the second measurement must be taken at least three hours after the first.

When the intersection of the two sextant position lines is plotted, it fixes our position at 43° 03'.6 N, 5° 55'.9 E. So just 0.7 miles (in 177°) separate the yacht's real position E (as established by coastal bearings) and the calculated position E' (obtained from the altitudes of the Sun).

This example shows just how accurately sextant altitudes can establish your position; you should find, with practice, that astronavigation is generally accurate to within 2-5 miles.

Note
It is also possible to take three sights. The boat will then be in the centre of a triangle formed by the intersection of the three position lines (point E')

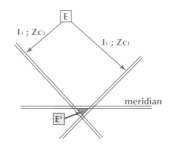

dd	mm	yy			U/T	10ʰ 05ᵐ 06ˢ		HB observed Sun
13	04	N+1						

L_e	±	43°.07166		Hs	50° 20'.0
D at 0h UT	±	8°.89166	Index error correction	⊖ 2'
p.p = UT x 0.9/60 Var 0'h in"	±	0°.15127	Other corrs. simplified	± 13'
D at UT	±	9°.04293	Ho	50° 31'.0
			-Hc	- 50° 30'.4
Sun, planet or γ			(sinHc = sin Le sin D + cos Le cos D cos LHA)	
GHA at 0h UT		179°.82333	I	⊕ 0'.6
Var at HAh in" 15°.003		151°.30526	Z_c	143.
- G_e	⊕-	5°.93166	cos Z = (sin D - sin Le sin Hc)/(cos Le cos Hc)	
(SHA*)			HB in east 180°<LHA Z_e=Z	HB in west LHA<180° Z_e=360°-Z
LHA at UT		337°.06025		

dd	mm	yy			U/T	14ʰ 03ᵐ 19ˢ		HB observed Sun
13	04	N+1						

L_e	±	43°.07166		Hs	43° 13'.5
D at 0h UT	±	8°.89166	Index error correction	⊖ 2'
p.p = UT x -0.9/60 Var 0'h in"	±	0°.21082	Other corrs. simplified	± 12'
D at UT	±	9°.10248	Ho	43° 23'.5
			-Hc	- 43° 23'.1
Sun, planet or γ			(sinHc = sin Le sin D + cos Le cos D cos LHA)	
GHA at 0h UT		179°.82333	I	⊕ 0'.4
Var at HAh in" 15°.003		210°.87133	Z_c	234.
- G_e	⊕-	5°.93166	cos Z = (sin D - sin Le sin Hc)/(cos Le cos Hc)	
(SHA*)			HB in east 180°<LHA Z_e=Z	HB in west LHA<180° Z_e=360°-Z
LHA at UT		36°.62632		

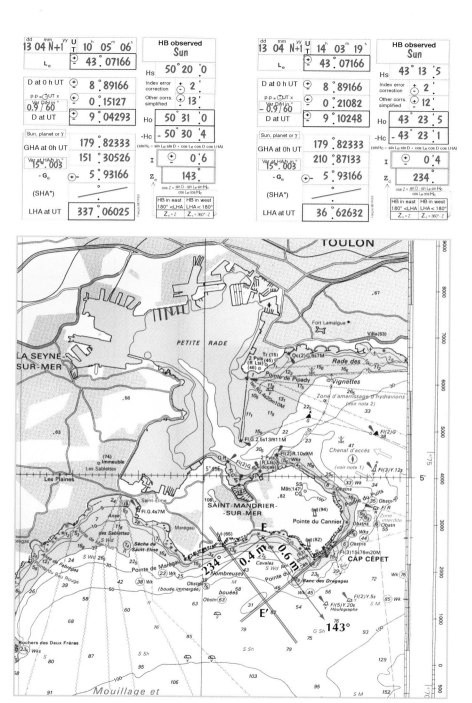

An extract from chart No 7406 courtesy of Service Hydrographique et Océanographique de la Marine. (Not to be used for navigation.)

An altitude position line moves, or transfers, at the speed of the boat, exactly the same as a transferred bearing in coastal navigation.

- From the boat's estimated position E1, we plot, after working out the sight, a first position line D1.
- Since the boat is steering 250° at 2 knots, the new estimated position is E2, derived from E1 by plotting a course of 250° for 6 miles.
- From the new estimate E2, we plot, after working out the sight, a second position line D2 in the same way.

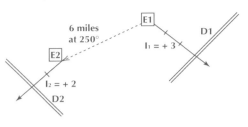

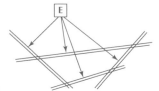

- The line D1 is transferred to D'1 in accordance with the vector of the boat's movement. The vector is shown by a dashed line; it has a length of 6 miles on a bearing of 250°. At a time t2, the boat is then at the intersection of D'1 and D2.

If we always build up altitude position lines D by using our latest estimated position as the assumed position, the geometry can all be constructed from this point (otherwise, it is not strictly correct to talk about transferring a position line). We label this current position E (and not E2, E3 or En). In this method, E is known as a timeless position because it serves as the pivot from which all the intercepts are plotted.

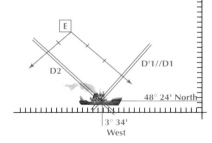

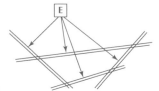

The latest estimated position E can be the point from which a large number of lines spread out like a beam of light.

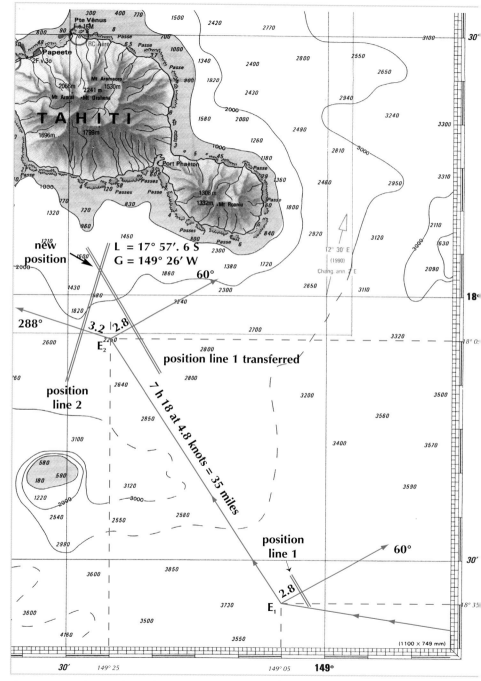

An extract from chart No 6688 courtesy of Service Hydrographique et Océanographique de la Marine. (Not to be used for navigation.)

From the estimated position E_1 (on the chart on page 87) which is 18° 35' S, 149° 05' W, a first position line gives an intercept of 2.8 miles on azimuth of 60°. After 7 hours 18 minutes, our estimated position is E_2 (18° 05' S, 149° 25' W) E_1 and E_2 are 35 miles apart.

A second position line established from E_2 gives an intercept of 3.2 miles on an azimuth of 288°. The vessel is positioned at the intersection of the first position line – transferred – and the second line, at 17° 57.6' S, 149° 26' W.

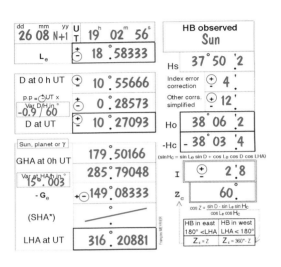

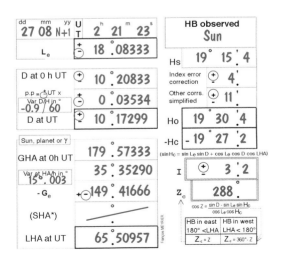

In practice, when you plot an altitude position line, the scale of the chart can be a problem. The length of a nautical mile on the chart is as follows:

scale	1 mile equivalent	scale	1 mile
1/20 000	9.26 cm	1/600 000	3.1 mm
1/25 000	7.40 cm	1/863 000	2.1 mm
1/50 000	3.70 cm	1/3 500 000	0.53 mm
1/116 500	1.59 cm	1/7 620 000	0.24 mm

It is out of the question to plot an intercept on charts where a nautical mile measures only 0.24mm. The solution, whenever the scale is too small, is to draw an enlargement of the area in which you are navigating on a separate sheet of paper. This enlargement is referred to as a plotting sheet.

THE PRINCIPLE OF THE PLOTTING SHEET

Without going into the theory of the Mercator chart (the principle of which is described on page 96), let us for the moment simply accept that any such chart, whatever its scale, has the following characteristics:

- The meridians (vertical lines on the chart) are parallel and equidistant
- The parallels of latitude (horizontal lines on the chart) are parallel to one another, but the distance between them increases towards the poles
- A constant course appears as a straight line

The distance between two parallels of latitude equals the distance between two meridians divided by cos L.

This explains why, as you move northwards, the vertical scale expands; so that as the latitude L increases from 0 to 90°, cos L decreases from 1 to 0, and 1/cos L increases from 1 to infinity.

To make the principle clear, angles and spacing have been exaggerated.

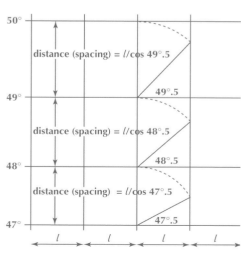

1 Take a sheet of paper covered with equally spaced lines (lined letter paper will do, but squared paper will not). Align the paper so the lines run from top to bottom, as in the diagram opposite. At the centre and near the bottom, draw one heavy vertical and one horizontal line.

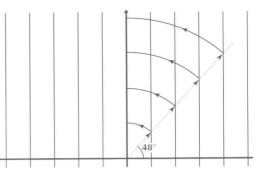

2 Since our latitude is about 48°, draw a dashed line at an angle of 48° to the horizontal. With a drawing compass, turn arcs back to the central vertical axis from the intersections of the diagonal line and the meridians. Where these arcs cut the axis, draw the parallels of latitude and you have a plotting sheet for part of a Mercator chart.

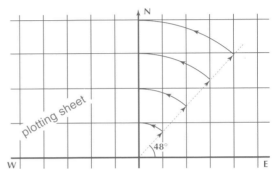

3 Rub out the diagonal line and you can plot intercepts and position lines directly on to this sheet.

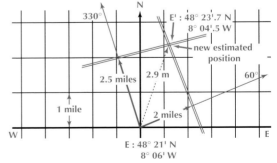

The plot is based on the estimated position E, ie 48° 21′ N, 8° 06′ W, which is placed in the centre.
First intercept: 2 miles on 60°.
Second intercept: 2.5 miles on 330°.
The old estimated position (E) and the new one (E') are 2.9 miles apart.

90

■■■ PLOTTING SHEET FOR A MERCATOR CHART (SECOND METHOD): ■■■
THE ANCILLARY CHART

Navigating offshore, it is possible to turn your plotting sheet into an ancillary chart covering 4° of latitude and 6-12° of longitude.

On this sheet you can plot your course, draw position lines and generally navigate for more than 400 miles, just as you would on a proper chart. Then from time to time you transfer the positions from the sheet to the real chart.

First you have to make the plotting sheet:
- Take a sheet of A3 paper.
- Place a graduated rose (in effect a compass rose) with a radius of about 6.5 cm on the left hand side of the sheet, equidistant from the top and bottom edges.
- Draw the two tangents, north and south, and another line through the centre.

- Extend the latitude scale one degree above and below the rose.
- Draw two more horizontal lines.

A plotting sheet like this covers 4 x 1° = 4 x 60′ = 240′ of latitude ie 240 miles:

- Draw a diagonal at an angle corresponding to the local latitude, say 48° N.
- This determines the first meridian (ie 13° W on the diagram below).
- Step by step, draw all the meridians, equidistant from one another.

Finally, all that's needed is to number the vaarious parallels of latitude (from 46° to 50°N) and meridians (from 6° to 15°W).

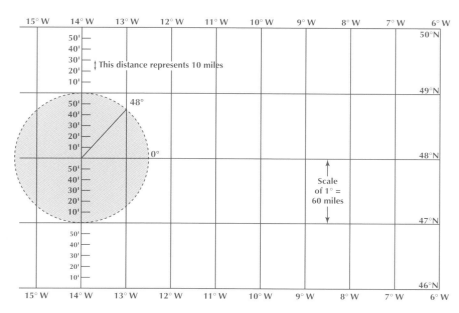

Imagine we are on an Atlantic crossing. We are making the return trip from Port Castries (14°.09 N, 61° W) on the island of Saint Lucia in the Antilles, to the Scilly Isles, where the Bishop Rock lighthouse (49° 52'.4 N, 6° 26' W) marks the entrance to the Channel.

The great circle distance is 3,401 miles (the rhumb line adds 42 miles) and we are using the SHOM passage chart No 6561S, which is the only one of its kind to cover the whole crossing (on a scale of 1/7 620000).

On a chart like this, 100 miles is represented by 2.4cm, so the plotting of altitude position lines would be extremely small; and since chart No 6561S is the only one available (there would be no point in SHOM. chopping up the North Atlantic into eight or ten charts), we plot our estimated positions on A3 plotting sheets or ancillary charts. With each sheet covering about 400 miles, we shall need eight of them for the whole North Atlantic.

Once a day, the positions on the plotting sheets will be transferred to the main chart so that we can visualise our daily progress.

Now, how do we mark our estimated positions on the plotting sheet? The crossing is almost completed, so to prepare the last sheet before making a landfall:

- Since we are heading north east, plot the approximate landfall directly on the sheet, by placing the Bishop Rock lighthouse in the top right hand corner

- Take 48° as the average latitude (the average meridian is the one passing through the centre of the rose)

- Draw equidistant meridians corresponding to the average latitude of 48° (as previously explained)

- Assemble the whole grid: latitudes extending over four degrees, from 46° N to 50° N, and longitudes over nine° from 6° W to 15° W

- Place the Bishop Rock lighthouse exactly at 49° 52min.4 N, 6° 26' W

On this sheet, we start from position A, the estimate for 06.00h on day J (position A was transferred from the preceding sheet).

- At 06.00h the intersection of position lines from Venus and Arcturus puts our yacht at A', the new starting point (the difference between A and A' is no doubt the result of a current of which we were unaware).

- Since day J was entirely cloudy, it was impossible to take any sights, and at 22.00h, position B is the result of the estimated ground track from A'. The distance made good from A' is 96 miles (22h - 6h = 16h at 6 knots), bringing the yacht to position B.

- At 22.00h, the intersection of position lines from Jupiter and Mars puts the yacht at B', which is the new estimated position.

- During the night of J to J+1, seven and a half knots was maintained for eight hours – that is 60 miles made good – to reach C at six o'clock the next morning, ie on day J+1.

- At six o'clock that morning, the intersection of position lines from Venus and Arcturus puts the yacht at C', which becomes the new estimated position.

- At 17.00h, towards the end of day J+1, we are at estimated position D, 111 miles from C' (17h - 6h = 11h at 10.1 knots = 111 miles made good).

- With a completely clear sky from morning to night, there is time to take three Sun sights. At 17.00, the time of the last sight, there is a cluster of two position lines and a noon sight.

The new estimated position is D' (at the centre of the triangle formed by the position lines), only 68 miles beyond the range of the Bishop Rock lighthouse, which should be within sight at about half past one in the morning if we can maintain a speed of eight knots (17.00h + 68 miles/8 knots = 1.30h). All times are UT.

Note
The position lines (7) and (8) are transferred to (7') and (8'), See the ancillary chart on pages 94 and 95.

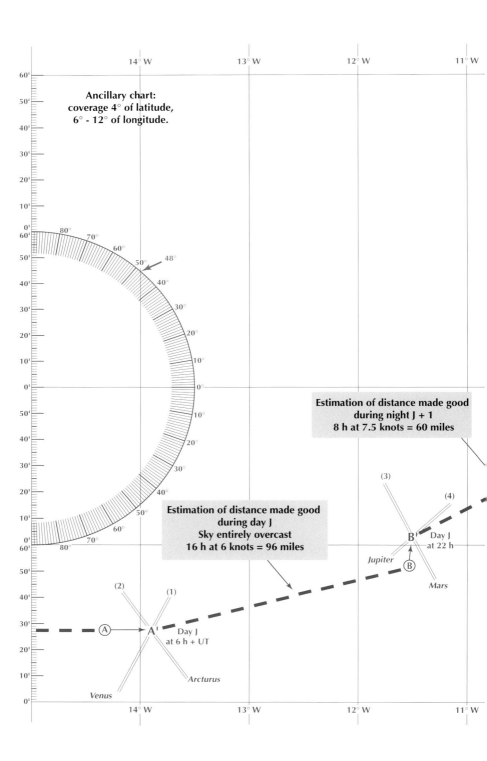

Ancillary chart:
coverage 4° of latitude,
6° - 12° of longitude.

Estimation of distance made good
during night J + 1
8 h at 7.5 knots = 60 miles

Estimation of distance made good
during day J
Sky entirely overcast
16 h at 6 knots = 96 miles

(3)

(4)

B' Day J
    at 22 h

Jupiter Ⓑ

Mars

(2)

(1)

Ⓐ → A' Day J
           at 6 h + UT

Arcturus

Venus

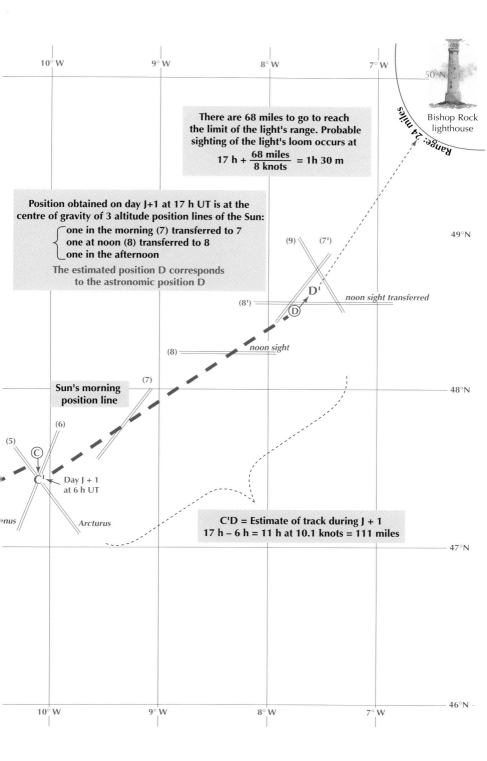

10° W   9° W   8° W   7° W
50°N

Bishop Rock lighthouse

Range: 24 miles

There are 68 miles to go to reach
the limit of the light's range. Probable
sighting of the light's loom occurs at

$$17\,h + \frac{68\ miles}{8\ knots} = 1h\ 30\ m$$

Position obtained on day J+1 at 17 h UT is at the
centre of gravity of 3 altitude position lines of the Sun:
  one in the morning (7) transferred to 7
  one at noon (8) transferred to 8
  one in the afternoon
The estimated position D corresponds
to the astronomic position D

49°N

(9)   (7')

(8')

D'

Ⓓ   noon sight transferred

(8)   noon sight

(7)

Sun's morning
position line

48°N

(6)

(5)

Ⓒ

C'   Day J + 1
at 6 h UT

·nus   Arcturus

C'D = Estimate of track during J + 1
17 h – 6 h = 11 h at 10.1 knots = 111 miles

47°N

46°N

10° W   9° W   8° W   7° W

In this type of projection, a sphere is represented by a cylinder in such a way that each point on the sphere has a projected image on the cylinder.

Imagine the Earth, with its centre at **O**, enclosed in a cylinder. Any position **c** on the sphere is represented by a position **C**, at the point where the extension of the dashed line **Oc** strikes the cylinder. So the projected images of the sphere's meridians are the vertical lines forming the cylinder, and the images of the parallels of latitude are perpendicular to them. When you unroll the cylinder it becomes a flat chart marked out with meridians and parallels.

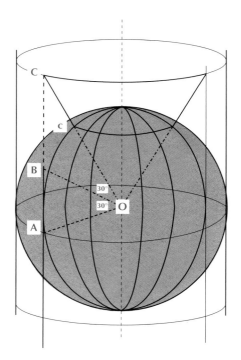

You will notice that:

- BC is much longer than AB (the latitudes increase) even though the two segments are formed from the same angle of 30°

- The poles have receded to infinity

Marine charts use the 'Mercator' projection, which differs very little from the cylindrical projection. The two projections are therefore often confused, and at first sight they are indeed similar, but in fact the latitudes increase in a different way.

Chapter 12

EXERCISES

We complete this introduction to the principle of the altitude position line with a series of 19 questions and answers followed in Chapter 13 by an exercise in the alternative method, using sight reduction tables. In these examples the sights are all assumed to be taken from a height of 2 metres and with an index error correction of 0'.

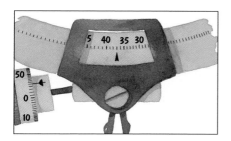

1 What does this sextant read?

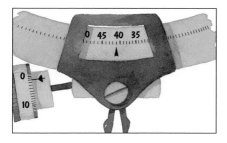

2 What does this sextant read?

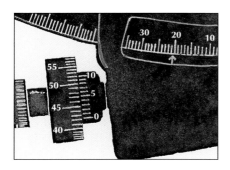

3 What does this sextant read?

4 What is the decimal equivalent of 9h 2m 8s ?

5 What is the decimal equivalent of 350° 38'.9 ?

6 What is the sexagesimal equivalent of 18h.98223 ?

7 What is the sexagesimal equivalent of 24°.32569 ?

8 Calculate 13h 26m 13s x 14°.999/h

9 Calculate sin 12°.23456

10 Calculate cos 67°.98765

11 Find the angle H whose sine = 0.43987

12 Find the angle Z whose cosine = -0.69832

13 On Thursday 9 July in the year N+1, at what time will the Sun reach its highest point along the meridian 5° 55'.9 E ?

14 What is the declination of the Sun at 13h 48m 12s on 30 March in the year N+1, at 43° N, 4° W ?

15 What is the Sun's local hour angle at 8h 01m 05s on the same day, at 42° 12'.2 N, 5° 57'.2 E?

16 Altitude position line from the Sun.
On 27 August in the year N+1, at 13h 47m 28s UT, from the estimated position 48° 56'.2 N, 2° 01'.7 W, we observe the Sun, from 2m above the water, at an altitude of 45° 50'.2. Plot the corresponding position line.

17 Position from two planet sights.
On 20 July in the year N+1, from the estimated position where L = 43° 04' N, and G = 5° 56' E, from a height of 2m: Saturn at 3h 32m 58s UT is at an altitude of 45° 26'.6; Jupiter at 3h 43m 19s UT is at an altitude of 44° 58'.6.

a) Plot the corresponding position lines.

b) Find the boat's position (we are assuming this is not possible without transferring between the two sights).

18 Position from two star sights.
On 17 August in the year N+1, from the estimated position where L = 43° 04' N, and G = 5° 56' E, from a height of 2m: Altair is at altitude 41° 33'.4 at 19h 05m 02s UT; Vega is at altitude 77° 30'.2 at 19h 26m 54s UT.

a) Plot the corresponding position lines.

b) Find the boat's position (we are assuming this is not possible without transferring between the two sights).

19 Position from two star sights.
On 21 April in the year N+1, from the estimated position where L = 43° 04' N, and G = 5° 56' E, from a height of 2m: Regulus is at 57° 08'.6 at 18h 57m 12s UT; Sirius is at 20° 26'.4 at 18h 58m 33s UT.

a) Plot the corresponding position lines.

b) Find the boat's position (we are assuming this is not possible without transferring between the two sights). You are given the GHA of the First Point of Aries at 0h UT on that day: 208° 51'.9.

ANSWERS

1 It reads 36° 55′.

2 It reads 41° 03′.

3 It reads 20° 42′.7.

4 9h 2m 8s = 9h.03555.

5 350° 38.9 = 350°.64833.

6 18h.98222 = 18h 58m 56s.

7 24°.32566 = 24° 19′.54.

8 13h 26m 13s x 14°.999/h
= 201°.54072.

9 sin 12°.23456 = 0.21191.

10 cos 67°.98765 = 0.37480.

11 (Questions 11 and 12, both on trigonometry, each have two answers)
If sin H = 0.43987, then H = 26°.09558 or H = 180° - 26°.09558 = 153°.90442.

12 If cos Z = -0.69832, then Z = 134°.29237 or Z = 360° -134°.29237 = 225°.70763.
In astro navigation, this uncertainty is resolved as follows: in dealing with altitude H, the acute angle of 26°.09558 is chosen when sights are taken facing the heavenly body;

whereas with azimuth Z, the correct value is 134°.29237 when a Sun sight is taken before midday or any sight is taken towards the east, and 225°.70763 when the Sun sight is after midday or any sight is taken towards the west.

13 On this particular day the Sun crosses the Greenwich meridian at T Pass = 12h 05m 11s. The Sun's speed at this moment is 14°.998/h. It will have reached an angle of -5° 59′.9 at -5°. 55′.9 divided by 14°.998/h, which equals -23m 44s. The Sun therefore crossed that meridian at 12h 05m 11s -23m 44s = 11h 41m 27s (note that because the observer is east of Greenwich, the Sun will reach its highest point above him long before it crosses the Greenwich meridian).

14 The Sun's declination is independent of the observer's position on Earth.

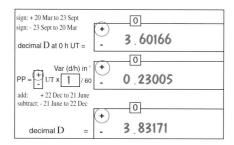

15 The local hour angle LHA depends on the observer's position (but only his longitude).

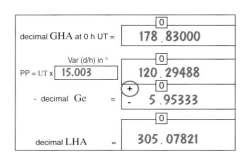

decimal GHA at 0 h UT = | 0 | 178 . 83000

PP = UT x | 15.003 | Var (d/h) in ° | 0 | 120 . 29488

(+) - decimal Ge = | 0 | - 5 . 95333

decimal LHA = | 0 | 305 . 07821

16 Altitude position line from the Sun.

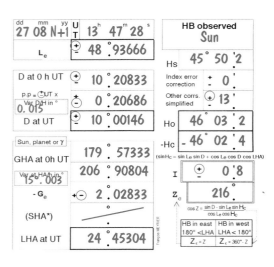

dd mm yy | U T | 27 08 N+1 | 13ʰ 47ᵐ 28ˢ

Lₑ | (+) - | 48 °.93666

D at 0 h UT | (+) - | 10 °.20833

p.p = ⊙UT x | 0.015 | Var D/H in ° | (+) - | 0 °.20686

D at UT | (+) - | 10 °.00146

Sun, planet or Ɣ

GHA at 0h UT | 179 °.57333

Var at HA/h in ° | 15°.003 | 206 °.90804

- Gₑ | +(-) | 2 °.02833

(SHA*)

LHA at UT | 24 °.45304

HB observed

Sun

Hs | 45° 50 '2

Index error correction | + - | 0 '

Other corrs. simplified | (+) | 13 '

Ho | 46° 03 '2

-Hc | - 46° 02 '4

(sin Hc = sin Le sin D + cos Le cos D cos LHA)

I | (+) - | 0 '8

Zc | 216 .

$\cos Z = \frac{\sin D - \sin Le \sin Hc}{\cos Le \cos Hc}$

HB in east	HB in west
180° <LHA	LHA < 180°
Zc = Z	Zc = 360° - Z

17 Position from two planet sights. The two position lines are plotted on the chart to give a new position at 43° 02'.8 N, 5° 58'.3 E. This new position is 2.1 miles from the previous one, using the assumed position for the calculations.

Hourly variation of D
d = 0'0

Hourly variation of GHA
15° + v
= 15° + 2', 4
= 15°. 04

Hourly variation of D
d = 0'0

Hourly variation of GHA
15° + v
= 15° + 2', 5
= 15°. 04166

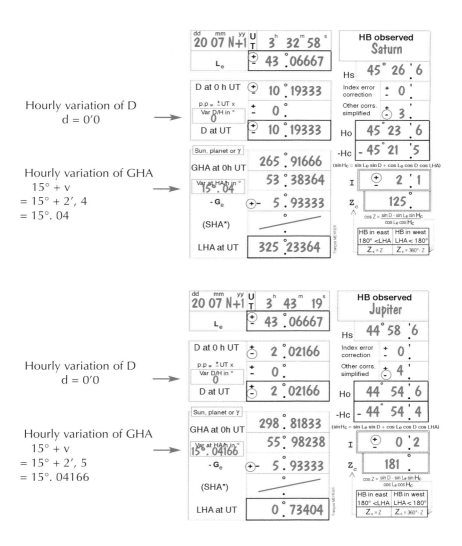

18 Position from two star sights. The two position lines are plotted on the chart to give a new position at 42° 51'.2 N, 5° 47'.9 E. This new position is 14.1 miles from the previous one, using the assumed position for the calculations.

Angular speed of γ ⟶

Angular speed of γ ⟶

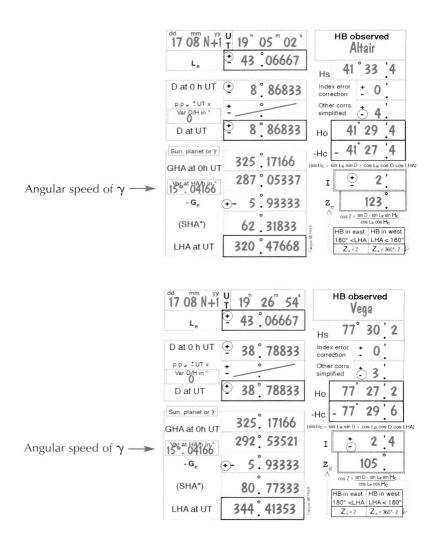

19 Position from two star sights. The two position lines are plotted on the chart to give a new position at 43° 06'.7 N, 5° 49'.8 E. This new position is 5.3 miles from the previous one, using the assumed position for the calculations.

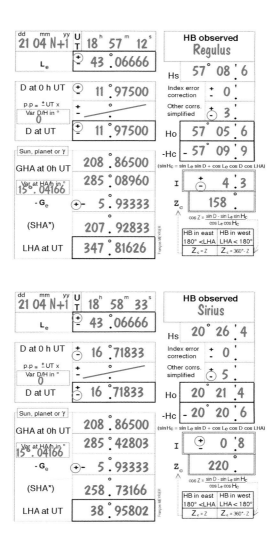

N. Lat. { LHA greater than 180°....Zn=Z / LHA less than 180°....Zn=360-Z

DECLINATION (15°-29°) CONTRARY NAME TO LATITUDE

The calculated altitude we are looking for is somewhere between Hc = 22° 54′ and Hc = 22° 54′ - 47′ = 22° 07′

With the two formulae Hc = sin L sin D + cos L cos D cos LHA and cosZ

$$\cos Z = \frac{\sin D - \sin L \sin Hc}{\cos L \cos Hc}$$

it is possible to predict Hc and Z for any local hour angle LHA, latitude L and declination D, expressed in whole numbers of degrees.

This is the purpose of the sight reduction tables HO249 which provide, for a limited number of positions on the globe, the precalculated altitudes Hc and angles Z of the heavenly bodies.

The positions for which these predictions have been calculated are those whose latitude L is a whole number of degrees and whose longitude G is such that LHA = GHA - L is a whole number of degrees.

These tables are very simple to use. They are currently available in the United States under the name HO249, and in the UK where they are known as AP3270. In France, there is a preference for the Dieumegard and Bataille tables, based on a different principle and less easy to use.

S. Lat. { LHA greater than 180°....Zn=180-Z / LHA less than 180°....Zn=180+Z

Chapter 13

THE ALTERNATIVE METHOD

Using the American sight reduction tables HO249, or the British equivalent AP3270, in the following example:

On 18 September, at 12h 43m 09s UT (10h 43m 09s local time) from an estimated position where L = 32° 12′ N, and G = 38° 25′ W, a corrected Sun sight gives a true altitude Ho of 22° 28′.

At the instant the altitude is measured, D = 21° 38′ S and GHA = 355° 48′. The aim of the exercise is to find the values of I and Zc.

In this method, instead of producing our intercept from an estimated position, we use an assumed or convenient position Pc, chosen so that:

a) its latitude is a whole number of degrees as near as possible to that of the estimated position, and

b) its longitude, as well as being near that of the estimated position, is such that its LHA is a whole number of degrees.

In this case, the co-ordinates of the convenient position Pc are: L = 32° N, G = 38° 48′ W.

Thirty-two is the nearest whole number to 32° 12′ (if the latitude L of the estimated position had been 32° 37′, we would have chosen 33° as the latitude of the convenient position). By giving G a value of 38° 48minutes W, we obtain a whole number for the LHA:

$$\begin{array}{r} GHA = 355° \ 48' \\ - \ G = 38° \ 48' \\ \hline LHA = 317° \end{array}$$

We now have the three keys to the basic formula: L = 32° N; LHA = 317°; D = 21° 38′ S.

■■■ ENTERING THE HO249 TABLES ■■■

a) Page   Latitude 32°
b) Page   Declination (15° - 29°) contrary name to latitude (D is south; L is north)

c) Line   LHA = 317°
d) Column   Declination 21°

Read off the precalculated values of Hc and Zc.

In the column D = 21°, the value of Hc = 22° 54′.
To obtain the value of Hc corresponding to 21° 38′ S, we have to interpolate to allow for the fact that as D changes from 21° to 22° Hc decreases by 47 minutes. The proportional part pp = -47′ x $\frac{38}{60}$ = -29′.8

Hc = 22° 54′ - 0° 29′.8 = 22° 24′.2
Intercept = Ho - Hc = 22° 28′S - 22° 24′.2 = I = 3.8 miles
Calculated azimuth = Zc = 137°
(In the American notation, Zc is written Zn, which means "Z from north")

Take care to follow the rules shown at the top and bottom of the tables. For HO249, they are not the same as those we used to calculate Zc, because the formula is different.

	LHA> 180° morning, heavenly body in the E	LHA< 180° afternoon, heavenly body in the W
Latitude north	Zn = Z	Zn = 360° - Z
Latitude south	Zn = 180° - Z	Zn = 180° + Z

Notes

1 In the d columns, the minus sign is not always printed on every line

2 In this method, because the assumed positions are not related to one another, it is the position lines which shift in accordance with the movement vectors.

EXTRACTS

Extracts from *L'Almanach du Marin Breton* (pages 108 to 113)
• Solar *Ephemerides*

Extracts from *Ephémérides Nautiques* (Bureau de Longitudes: Editions Edinautic) (pages 114 to 116)
• Page of *Ephemerides* for 20 July
• Pages of *Ephemerides* for 21 April and 17 August
• Equatorial co-ordinates of the stars

Notation

In the French official publications, hour angle notation varies according to the heavenly body being observed. This notation is included here as an aid to using the tables on pages 108 to 113.

Hour angles counted from the Greenwich meridian: GHA	Local Hour Angles counted from G, the meridian of longitude: LHA = GHA - G

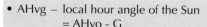

• AHvo – hour angle of the Sun • AHao – hour angle of the planets • AHso – hour angle of the First Point of Aries γ • AHao – hour angle of the Moon	• AHvg – local hour angle of the Sun = AHvo - G • AHag – local hour angle of the planets = AHvo - G • AHsg – local hour angle of the First Point of Aries γ = AHso - G • AHag – local hour angle of the Moon = AHao - G

To avoid newcomers to the subject being confused by numerous different symbols, the notation and terminology have been changed throughout from that used in official French publications such as the *Ephémérides Nautiques*, to the straightforward notation that the British and Americans use in their almanacs (see Main Abbreviations, pages 118-120).

Hour angles are denoted as follows:

Greenwich Hour Angle = GHA
(equivalent to the French *angle horaire Greenwich*, AHG)

Local hour Angle = LHA (equivalent to *angle horaire local*, AHL)

Using this simple notation, which applies equally to the Sun, moon, planets and the stars, the local hour angle of a star is written as:

$$LHA* = GHA\ \gamma - G + SHA*$$

Extracts from *L'Almanach du Marin Breton*

Year N

Janvier

Janv.		Déclinaison à 0 h U.T. ° '	d '	AHvo à 0 h U.T. ° '	V o	T. Pass. U.T. h. mn. s.	Lever U.T. h. mn.	Coucher U.T. h. mn.
1	M	23 00,8S	0,2	179 08,8		12 03 39	7 59	16 09
2	J	22 55,7		179 01,8		12 04 07	7 58	16 10
3	V	22 50,1		178 54,8	14,995	12 04 34	7 58	16 11
4	S	22 44,1		178 47,9		12 05 02	7 58	16 12
5	D	22 37,7	0,3	178 41,1		12 05 29	7 58	16 13
6	L	22 30,8		178 34,4		12 05 55	7 58	16 15
7	M	22 23,4		178 27,9		12 06 21	7 57	16 16
8	M	22 15,6		178 21,4		12 06 47	7 57	16 17
9	J	22 07,4		178 15,1		12 07 12	7 56	16 18
10	V	21 58,7		178 08,9		12 07 37	7 56	16 20
11	S	21 49,6	0,4	178 02,8	14,996	12 08 01	7 55	16 21
12	D	21 40,1		177 56,9		12 08 24	7 55	16 22
13	L	21 30,2		177 51,2		12 08 47	7 54	16 24
14	M	21 19,8		177 45,6		12 09 09	7 53	16 25
15	M	21 09,1		177 40,2		12 09 30	7 53	16 27
16	J	20 57,9		177 34,9		12 09 51	7 52	16 28
17	V	20 46,3	0,5	177 29,8		12 10 10	7 51	16 30
18	S	20 34,4		177 25,0		12 10 30	7 50	16 31
19	D	20 22,0		177 20,2		12 10 48	7 49	16 33
20	L	20 09,3		177 15,7	14,997	12 11 06	7 48	16 34
21	M	19 56,2		177 11,4		12 11 23	7 47	16 36
22	M	19 42,7		177 07,3		12 11 39	7 46	16 38
23	J	19 28,9		177 03,3		12 11 54	7 45	16 39
24	V	19 14,7	0,6	176 59,6		12 12 09	7 44	16 41
25	S	19 00,1		176 56,0		12 12 23	7 43	16 42
26	D	18 45,2		176 52,7		12 12 36	7 42	16 44
27	L	18 29,9		176 49,5	14,998	12 12 48	7 40	16 46
28	M	18 14,3		176 46,5		12 12 59	7 39	16 47
29	M	17 58,4	0,7	176 43,8		12 13 10	7 38	16 49
30	J	17 42,2		176 41,2		12 13 20	7 36	16 51
31	V	17 25,6S		176 38,9	14,999	12 13 29	7 35	16 53

Février

Fév.		Déclinaison à 0 h U.T. ° '	d '	AHvo à 0 h U.T. ° '	V o	T. Pass. U.T. h. mn. s.	Lever U.T. h. mn.	Coucher U.T. h. mn.
1	S	17 08,8S		176 36,7		12 13 37	7 34	16 54
2	D	16 51,6	0,7	176 34,7		12 13 45	7 32	16 56
3	L	16 34,1		176 33,0	14,999	12 13 51	7 31	16 58
4	M	16 16,4		176 31,4		12 13 57	7 29	16 59
5	M	15 58,3		176 30,1		12 14 02	7 28	17 01
6	J	15 40,0		176 28,9		12 14 06	7 26	17 03
7	V	15 21,4		176 27,9		12 14 10	7 24	17 05
8	S	15 02,6		176 27,2		12 14 12	7 23	17 06
9	D	14 43,5	0,8	176 26,6		12 14 14	7 21	17 08
10	L	14 24,2		176 26,2		12 14 15	7 19	17 10
11	M	14 04,6		176 26,0	15,000	12 14 16	7 18	17 12
12	M	13 44,8		176 26,1		12 14 15	7 16	17 13
13	J	13 24,7		176 26,3		12 14 14	7 14	17 15
14	V	13 04,5		176 26,7		12 14 12	7 12	17 17
15	S	12 44,0		176 27,3		12 14 09	7 11	17 18
16	D	12 23,3		176 28,1		12 14 06	7 09	17 20
17	L	12 02,5		176 29,0		12 14 01	7 07	17 22
18	M	11 41,4		176 30,2	15,001	12 13 56	7 05	17 24
19	M	11 20,2		176 31,5		12 13 51	7 03	17 25
20	J	10 58,7		176 33,0		12 13 45	7 01	17 27
21	V	10 37,1		176 34,7		12 13 38	6 59	17 29
22	S	10 15,4	0,9	176 36,5		12 13 30	6 57	17 30
23	D	9 53,5		176 38,5		12 13 22	6 55	17 32
24	L	9 31,4		176 40,6		12 13 13	6 54	17 34
25	M	9 09,2		176 42,9		12 13 03	6 52	17 35
26	M	8 46,9		176 45,3		12 12 53	6 50	17 37
27	J	8 24,4		176 47,9	15,002	12 12 43	6 48	17 39
28	V	8 01,8S		176 50,6		12 12 32	6 45	17 40

Mars

Mars		Déclinaison à 0 h U.T. ° '	d '	AHvo à 0 h U.T. ° '	V o	T. Pass. U.T. h. mn. s.	Lever U.T. h. mn.	Coucher U.T. h. mn.
1	S	7 39,1S		176 53,4		12 12 20	6 43	17 42
2	D	7 16,2		176 56,3		12 12 08	6 41	17 44
3	L	6 53,3		176 59,4		12 11 56	6 39	17 45
4	M	6 30,3		177 02,6	15,002	12 11 43	6 37	17 47
5	M	6 07,1		177 05,9		12 11 29	6 35	17 49
6	J	5 43,9		177 09,3		12 11 16	6 33	17 50
7	V	5 20,6		177 12,8		12 11 02	6 31	17 52
8	S	4 57,3		177 16,4		12 10 47	6 29	17 54
9	D	4 33,9		177 20,0		12 10 32	6 27	17 55
10	L	4 10,4		177 23,8		12 10 17	6 25	17 57
11	M	3 46,8		177 27,7		12 10 01	6 22	17 59
12	M	3 23,2		177 31,6	15,003	12 09 45	6 20	18 00
13	J	2 59,6		177 35,6		12 09 29	6 18	18 02
14	V	2 36,0		177 39,7		12 09 13	6 16	18 03
15	S	2 12,3		177 43,9		12 08 56	6 14	18 05
16	D	1 48,6	1,0	177 48,1		12 08 39	6 12	18 07
17	L	1 24,9		177 52,4		12 08 21	6 10	18 08
18	M	1 01,2		177 56,7		12 08 04	6 07	18 10
19	M	0 37,5		178 01,1	15,003	12 07 46	6 05	18 11
20	J	0 13,7S		178 05,6		12 07 29	6 03	18 13
21	V	0 10,0N		178 10,0		12 07 11	6 01	18 15
22	S	0 33,6		178 14,5		12 06 53	5 59	18 16
23	D	0 57,3		178 19,0		12 06 35	5 56	18 18
24	L	1 20,9		178 23,6		12 06 16	5 54	18 19
25	M	1 44,5		178 28,1		12 05 58	5 52	18 21
26	M	2 08,1		178 32,7		12 05 40	5 50	18 22
27	J	2 31,6		178 37,3		12 05 22	5 48	18 24
28	V	2 55,1		178 41,8		12 05 03	5 46	18 26
29	S	3 18,5		178 46,4		12 04 45	5 43	18 27
30	D	3 41,8		178 50,9		12 04 27	5 41	18 29
31	L	4 05,1N		178 55,4		12 04 09	5 39	18 30

Avril

Avril		Déclinaison à 0 h U.T. ° '	d '	AHvo à 0 h U.T. ° '	V o	T. Pass. U.T. h. mn. s.	Lever U.T. h. mn.	Coucher U.T. h. mn.
1	M	4 28,3N		178 59,9		12 03 51	5 37	18 32
2	M	4 51,5	1,0	179 04,4		12 03 33	5 35	18 33
3	J	5 14,5		179 08,8		12 03 16	5 33	18 35
4	V	5 37,4		179 13,2		12 02 58	5 30	18 37
5	S	6 00,3		179 17,5		12 02 41	5 28	18 38
6	D	6 23,0		179 21,8		12 02 24	5 26	18 40
7	L	6 45,7		179 26,0		12 02 07	5 24	18 41
8	M	7 08,2		179 30,2	15,003	12 01 51	5 22	18 43
9	M	7 30,6		179 34,4		12 01 34	5 20	18 44
10	J	7 52,9		179 38,4		12 01 18	5 18	18 46
11	V	8 15,0		179 42,4		12 01 02	5 16	18 48
12	S	8 37,0	0,9	179 46,4		12 00 47	5 14	18 49
13	D	8 58,9		179 50,2		12 00 31	5 11	18 51
14	L	9 20,6		179 54,0		12 00 16	5 09	18 52
15	M	9 42,1		179 57,7		12 00 02	5 07	18 54
16	M	10 03,5		180 01,3		11 59 47	5 05	18 55
17	J	10 24,8		180 04,9		11 59 33	5 03	18 57
18	V	10 45,8		180 08,4		11 59 20	5 01	18 58
19	S	11 06,7		180 11,7		11 59 07	4 59	19 00
20	D	11 27,4		180 14,9		11 58 54	4 57	19 02
21	L	11 47,9		180 18,1		11 58 41	4 55	19 03
22	M	12 08,2		180 21,1	15,002	11 58 29	4 53	19 05
23	M	12 28,3		180 24,1		11 58 18	4 51	19 06
24	J	12 48,2		180 26,9		11 58 07	4 49	19 08
25	V	13 07,8	0,8	180 29,6		11 57 56	4 48	19 09
26	S	13 27,3		180 32,1		11 57 46	4 46	19 11
27	D	13 46,6		180 34,6		11 57 37	4 44	19 12
28	L	14 05,6		180 36,9		11 57 28	4 42	19 14
29	M	14 24,4		180 39,1		11 57 19	4 40	19 16
30	M	14 43,0N		180 41,2	15,001	11 57 11	4 38	19 17

Extracts from *L'Almanach du Marin Breton*

Year N

Mai		Déclinaison à 0 h U.T. (° ')	d (')	AHvo à 0 h U.T. (° ')	V (o)	T. Pass. U.T. (h. mn. s.)	Lever (h. mn.)	Coucher (h. mn.)
1	J	15 01,3N	0,8	180 43,1		11 57 04	4 37	19 19
2	V	15 19,3		180 44,9		11 56 57	4 35	19 20
3	S	15 37,2		180 46,5		11 56 51	4 33	19 22
4	D	15 54,7		180 48,0	15,001	11 56 45	4 31	19 23
5	L	16 12,0		180 49,4		11 56 40	4 30	19 25
6	M	16 29,0	0,7	180 50,6		11 56 35	4 28	19 26
7	M	16 45,8		180 51,6		11 56 31	4 26	19 28
8	J	17 02,3		180 52,6		11 56 28	4 25	19 29
9	V	17 18,5		180 53,4		11 56 25	4 23	19 31
10	S	17 34,4		180 54,0		11 56 23	4 22	19 32
11	D	17 50,0		180 54,5		11 56 21	4 20	19 34
12	L	18 05,3		180 54,9		11 56 20	4 19	19 35
13	M	18 20,3		180 55,1	15,000	11 56 19	4 17	19 37
14	M	18 35,0	0,6	180 55,2		11 56 19	4 16	19 38
15	J	18 49,3		180 55,2		11 56 19	4 14	19 39
16	V	19 03,4		180 55,0		11 56 20	4 13	19 41
17	S	19 17,1		180 54,7		11 56 22	4 12	19 42
18	D	19 30,6		180 54,2		11 56 24	4 10	19 43
19	L	19 43,6		180 53,6		11 56 27	4 09	19 45
20	M	19 56,4		180 52,9		11 56 30	4 08	19 46
21	M	20 08,8	0,5	180 52,0		11 56 34	4 06	19 47
22	J	20 20,8		180 51,0		11 56 38	4 05	19 49
23	V	20 32,5		180 49,9		11 56 43	4 04	19 50
24	S	20 43,9		180 48,7		11 56 48	4 03	19 51
25	D	20 54,9		180 47,3	14,999	11 56 54	4 02	19 52
26	L	21 05,5		180 45,8		11 57 00	4 01	19 54
27	M	21 15,8		180 44,2		11 57 07	4 00	19 55
28	M	21 25,7	0,4	180 42,4		11 57 14	3 59	19 56
29	J	21 35,2		180 40,5		11 57 22	3 58	19 57
30	V	21 44,3		180 38,5		11 57 30	3 57	19 58
31	S	21 53,2N		180 36,4	14,998	11 57 38	3 57	19 59

Juin		Déclinaison à 0 h U.T. (° ')	d (')	AHvo à 0 h U.T. (° ')	V (o)	T. Pass. U.T. (h. mn. s.)	Lever (h. mn.)	Coucher (h. mn.)
1	D	22 01,6N		180 34,2		11 57 48	3 56	20 00
2	L	22 09,6		180 31,9		11 57 57	3 55	20 01
3	M	22 17,3	0,3	180 29,5		11 58 07	3 55	20 02
4	M	22 24,5		180 27,0		11 58 17	3 54	20 03
5	J	22 31,4		180 24,4		11 58 28	3 53	20 04
6	V	22 37,8		180 21,7		11 58 39	3 53	20 05
7	S	22 43,9		180 18,9		11 58 50	3 52	20 06
8	D	22 49,6		180 16,1		11 59 01	3 52	20 07
9	L	22 54,8	0,2	180 13,2		11 59 13	3 52	20 07
10	M	22 59,7		180 10,2		11 59 25	3 51	20 08
11	M	23 04,1		180 07,2		11 59 37	3 51	20 09
12	J	23 08,2		180 04,2		11 59 49	3 51	20 09
13	V	23 11,8		180 01,1		12 00 02	3 50	20 10
14	S	23 15,1		179 57,9		12 00 14	3 50	20 10
15	D	23 17,9	0,1	179 54,7	14,998	12 00 27	3 50	20 11
16	L	23 20,3		179 51,6		12 00 40	3 50	20 11
17	M	23 22,3		179 48,3		12 00 53	3 50	20 12
18	M	23 23,9		179 45,1		12 01 06	3 50	20 12
19	J	23 25,1		179 41,9		12 01 19	3 50	20 12
20	V	23 25,9	0,0	179 38,6		12 01 32	3 50	20 13
21	S	23 26,2		179 35,4		12 01 45	3 51	20 13
22	D	23 26,1		179 32,2		12 01 58	3 51	20 13
23	L	23 25,7		179 29,0		12 02 10	3 51	20 13
24	M	23 24,8		179 25,7		12 02 23	3 51	20 13
25	M	23 23,5		179 22,6		12 02 36	3 52	20 13
26	J	23 21,8	0,1	179 19,4		12 02 49	3 52	20 13
27	V	23 19,6		179 16,3		12 03 01	3 53	20 13
28	S	23 17,1		179 13,2		12 03 13	3 53	20 13
29	D	23 14,2		179 10,1		12 03 25	3 54	20 13
30	L	23 10,8N	0,2	179 07,1		12 03 37	3 54	20 13

Juillet		Déclinaison à 0 h U.T. (° ')	d (')	AHvo à 0 h U.T. (° ')	V (o)	T. Pass. U.T. (h. mn. s.)	Lever (h. mn.)	Coucher (h. mn.)
1	M	23 07,0N		179 04,1		12 03 49	3 55	20 12
2	M	23 02,9		179 01,2		12 04 01	3 56	20 12
3	J	22 58,3	0,2	178 58,4		12 04 12	3 56	20 12
4	V	22 53,4		178 55,6		12 04 23	3 57	20 11
5	S	22 48,0		178 53,0	14,998	12 04 33	3 58	20 11
6	D	22 42,2		178 50,4		12 04 43	3 59	20 10
7	L	22 36,1		178 47,9		12 04 53	4 00	20 10
8	M	22 29,5		178 45,4		12 05 03	4 00	20 09
9	M	22 22,6	0,3	178 43,1		12 05 12	4 01	20 09
10	J	22 15,3		178 40,9		12 05 20	4 02	20 08
11	V	22 07,6		178 38,8		12 05 29	4 03	20 07
12	S	21 59,5		178 36,8		12 05 36	4 04	20 06
13	D	21 51,0		178 35,0		12 05 43	4 05	20 06
14	L	21 42,2		178 33,2		12 05 50	4 06	20 05
15	M	21 33,0	0,4	178 31,6	14,999	12 05 56	4 07	20 04
16	M	21 23,4		178 30,2		12 06 02	4 09	20 03
17	J	21 13,5		178 28,8		12 06 07	4 10	20 02
18	V	21 03,2		178 27,6		12 06 12	4 11	20 01
19	S	20 52,6		178 26,5		12 06 16	4 12	20 00
20	D	20 41,6		178 25,6		12 06 19	4 13	19 59
21	L	20 30,2		178 24,8		12 06 22	4 15	19 57
22	M	20 18,5	0,5	178 24,1		12 06 25	4 16	19 56
23	M	20 06,5		178 23,6		12 06 26	4 17	19 55
24	J	19 54,1		178 23,2		12 06 28	4 18	19 54
25	V	19 41,4		178 23,0	15,000	12 06 28	4 20	19 52
26	S	19 28,4		178 22,9		12 06 28	4 21	19 51
27	D	19 15,1		178 22,9		12 06 28	4 22	19 50
28	L	19 01,4		178 23,1		12 06 27	4 24	19 48
29	M	18 47,4	0,6	178 23,4		12 06 25	4 25	19 47
30	M	18 33,1		178 23,9		12 06 23	4 26	19 45
31	J	18 18,5N		178 24,6	15,001	12 06 20	4 28	19 44

Août		Déclinaison à 0 h U.T. (° ')	d (')	AHvo à 0 h U.T. (° ')	V (o)	T. Pass. U.T. (h. mn. s.)	Lever (h. mn.)	Coucher (h. mn.)
1	V	18 03,6N	0,6	178 25,3		12 06 17	4 29	19 42
2	S	17 48,4		178 26,3		12 06 13	4 31	19 41
3	D	17 32,9		178 27,3		12 06 08	4 32	19 39
4	L	17 17,2		178 28,6		12 06 03	4 33	19 38
5	M	17 01,1		178 30,0	15,001	12 05 57	4 35	19 36
6	M	16 44,8		178 31,5		12 05 51	4 36	19 34
7	J	16 28,2	0,7	178 33,2		12 05 43	4 38	19 33
8	V	16 11,3		178 35,0		12 05 36	4 39	19 31
9	S	15 54,2		178 37,0		12 05 28	4 41	19 29
10	D	15 36,8		178 39,1		12 05 19	4 42	19 27
11	L	15 19,2		178 41,4		12 05 09	4 44	19 25
12	M	15 01,4		178 43,9		12 04 59	4 45	19 24
13	M	14 43,3		178 46,4		12 04 49	4 47	19 22
14	J	14 24,9		178 49,2	15,002	12 04 38	4 48	19 20
15	V	14 06,4		178 52,0		12 04 26	4 50	19 18
16	S	13 47,6		178 55,0		12 04 14	4 51	19 16
17	D	13 28,6	0,8	178 58,1		12 04 01	4 53	19 15
18	L	13 09,3		179 01,4		12 03 48	4 54	19 13
19	M	12 49,9		179 04,8		12 03 34	4 55	19 11
20	M	12 30,3		179 08,3		12 03 19	4 57	19 09
21	J	12 10,5		179 11,9		12 03 05	4 58	19 07
22	V	11 50,4		179 15,6		12 02 50	5 00	19 05
23	S	11 30,2		179 19,5		12 02 34	5 01	19 03
24	D	11 09,8		179 23,4		12 02 18	5 03	19 01
25	L	10 49,2		179 27,5	15,003	12 02 02	5 04	18 59
26	M	10 28,5		179 31,6		12 01 45	5 06	18 57
27	M	10 07,6	0,9	179 35,9		12 01 28	5 07	18 55
28	J	9 46,5		179 40,2		12 01 10	5 09	18 52
29	V	9 25,3		179 44,7		12 00 52	5 10	18 50
30	S	9 03,9		179 49,2		12 00 34	5 12	18 48
31	D	8 42,4N		179 53,8		12 00 16	5 13	18 46

Extracts from *L'Almanach du Marin Breton*

Year N

Sept.

Sept.		Déclinaison à 0 h U.T.	d	AHvo à 0 h U.T.	V	T. Pass. U.T. h. mn. s.	Lever U.T. h. mn.	Coucher U.T. h. mn.
1	L	8 20,7N		179 58,4		11 59 57	5 15	18 44
2	M	7 58,9		180 03,2		11 59 38	5 16	18 42
3	M	7 37,0		180 08,0		11 59 18	5 18	18 40
4	J	7 14,9		180 12,9	15,003	11 58 59	5 19	18 38
5	V	6 52,8	0,9	180 17,8		11 58 39	5 21	18 35
6	S	6 30,5		180 22,8		11 58 19	5 22	18 33
7	D	6 08,1		180 27,9		11 57 58	5 24	18 31
8	L	5 45,6		180 33,0		11 57 38	5 25	18 29
9	M	5 23,0		180 38,1		11 57 17	5 27	18 27
10	M	5 00,3		180 43,4		11 56 56	5 28	18 25
11	J	4 37,6		180 48,6		11 56 35	5 30	18 22
12	V	4 14,7		180 53,9		11 56 14	5 31	18 20
13	S	3 51,8		180 59,2		11 55 52	5 33	18 18
14	D	3 28,9		181 04,5		11 55 31	5 34	18 16
15	L	3 05,8		181 09,9		11 55 10	5 36	18 14
16	M	2 42,7		181 15,2		11 54 48	5 37	18 11
17	M	2 19,6		181 20,6	15,004	11 54 27	5 39	18 09
18	J	1 56,4		181 26,0		11 54 05	5 40	18 07
19	V	1 33,2		181 31,3		11 53 44	5 42	18 05
20	S	1 09,9	1,0	181 36,7		11 53 22	5 43	18 03
21	D	0 46,6		181 42,0		11 53 01	5 45	18 00
22	L	0 23,3N		181 47,3		11 52 40	5 46	17 58
23	M	0 00,1S		181 52,6		11 52 19	5 48	17 56
24	M	0 23,4		181 57,9		11 51 58	5 49	17 54
25	J	0 46,8		182 03,1		11 51 37	5 51	17 52
26	V	1 10,2		182 08,2		11 51 17	5 52	17 49
27	S	1 33,6		182 13,3		11 50 56	5 54	17 47
28	D	1 56,9		182 18,4		11 50 36	5 55	17 45
29	L	2 20,3		182 23,4	15,003	11 50 16	5 57	17 43
30	M	2 43,6S		182 28,3		11 49 57	5 58	17 41

Oct.

Oct.		Déclinaison à 0 h U.T.	d	AHvo à 0 h U.T.	V	T. Pass. U.T. h. mn. s.	Lever U.T. h. mn.	Coucher U.T. h. mn.
1	M	3 06,9S		182 33,2		11 49 37	6 00	17 39
2	J	3 30,2		182 38,0		11 49 18	6 01	17 36
3	V	3 53,4		182 42,7		11 49 00	6 03	17 34
4	S	4 16,6		182 47,4		11 48 41	6 04	17 32
5	D	4 39,7	1,0	182 51,9		11 48 23	6 06	17 30
6	L	5 02,8		182 56,4		11 48 06	6 08	17 28
7	M	5 25,8		183 00,8	15,003	11 47 48	6 09	17 26
8	M	5 48,7		183 05,1		11 47 31	6 11	17 23
9	J	6 11,6		183 09,2		11 47 15	6 12	17 21
10	V	6 34,4		183 13,3		11 46 59	6 14	17 19
11	S	6 57,0		183 17,3		11 46 43	6 15	17 17
12	D	7 19,6		183 21,1		11 46 28	6 17	17 15
13	L	7 42,1		183 24,8		11 46 13	6 19	17 13
14	M	8 04,5		183 28,4		11 45 59	6 20	17 11
15	M	8 26,8		183 31,9		11 45 46	6 22	17 09
16	J	8 48,9		183 35,2		11 45 33	6 23	17 07
17	V	9 11,0		183 38,4		11 45 20	6 25	17 05
18	S	9 32,9	0,9	183 41,5	15,002	11 45 08	6 27	17 03
19	D	9 54,6		183 44,3		11 44 57	6 28	17 01
20	L	10 16,2		183 47,1		11 44 46	6 30	16 59
21	M	10 37,7		183 49,6		11 44 37	6 31	16 57
22	M	10 59,0		183 52,0		11 44 27	6 33	16 55
23	J	11 20,2		183 54,2		11 44 19	6 35	16 53
24	V	11 41,1		183 56,3		11 44 11	6 36	16 51
25	S	12 01,9		183 58,2		11 44 04	6 38	16 49
26	D	12 22,6		183 59,8	15,001	11 43 57	6 40	16 48
27	L	12 43,0		184 01,3		11 43 52	6 41	16 46
28	M	13 03,2		184 02,6		11 43 47	6 43	16 44
29	M	13 23,3	0,8	184 03,8		11 43 43	6 45	16 42
30	J	13 43,1		184 04,7		11 43 40	6 46	16 40
31	V	14 02,7S		184 05,4	15,000	11 43 37	6 48	16 39

Nov.

Nov.		Déclinaison à 0 h U.T.	d	AHvo à 0 h U.T.	V	T. Pass. U.T. h. mn. s.	Lever U.T. h. mn.	Coucher U.T. h. mn.
1	S	14 22,1S		184 05,9		11 43 35	6 50	16 37
2	D	14 41,2		184 06,3		11 43 34	6 51	16 35
3	L	15 00,1	0,8	184 06,4	15,000	11 43 34	6 53	16 34
4	M	15 18,8		184 06,3		11 43 35	6 55	16 32
5	M	15 37,2		184 06,1		11 43 36	6 56	16 30
6	J	15 55,4		184 05,6		11 43 39	6 58	16 29
7	V	16 13,3		184 04,9		11 43 42	7 00	16 27
8	S	16 30,9		184 04,0		11 43 46	7 01	16 26
9	D	16 48,2		184 02,9	14,999	11 43 50	7 03	16 24
10	L	17 05,3	0,7	184 01,6		11 43 56	7 05	16 23
11	M	17 22,0		184 00,1		11 44 02	7 06	16 21
12	M	17 38,5		183 58,4		11 44 10	7 08	16 20
13	J	17 54,6		183 56,5		11 44 18	7 09	16 19
14	V	18 10,5		183 54,4		11 44 27	7 11	16 17
15	S	18 26,0		183 52,1		11 44 36	7 13	16 16
16	D	18 41,2		183 49,5	14,998	11 44 47	7 14	16 15
17	L	18 56,1		183 46,7		11 44 59	7 16	16 14
18	M	19 10,6	0,6	183 43,8		11 45 11	7 18	16 12
19	M	19 24,8		183 40,6		11 45 24	7 19	16 11
20	J	19 38,7		183 37,2		11 45 38	7 21	16 10
21	V	19 52,1		183 33,6		11 45 53	7 22	16 09
22	S	20 05,3		183 29,8		11 46 08	7 24	16 08
23	D	20 18,0		183 25,8	14,997	11 46 25	7 25	16 07
24	L	20 30,4	0,5	183 21,6		11 46 42	7 27	16 06
25	M	20 42,4		183 17,1		11 47 00	7 28	16 05
26	M	20 54,0		183 12,5		11 47 19	7 30	16 04
27	J	21 05,3		183 07,8		11 47 38	7 31	16 04
28	V	21 16,1		183 02,8		11 47 59	7 33	16 03
29	S	21 26,5	0,4	182 57,6	14,996	11 48 20	7 34	16 02
30	D	21 36,6S		182 52,3		11 48 41	7 35	16 02

Déc.

Déc.		Déclinaison à 0 h U.T.	d	AHvo à 0 h U.T.	V	T. Pass. U.T. h. mn. s.	Lever U.T. h. mn.	Coucher U.T. h. mn.
1	L	21 46,2S		182 46,8		11 49 04	7 37	16 01
2	M	21 55,4	0,4	182 41,1		11 49 27	7 38	16 01
3	M	22 04,2		182 35,3		11 49 50	7 39	16 00
4	J	22 12,5		182 29,4	14,996	11 50 14	7 41	16 00
5	V	22 20,5	0,3	182 23,3		11 50 39	7 42	15 59
6	S	22 28,0		182 17,0		11 51 04	7 43	15 59
7	D	22 35,0		182 10,7		11 51 30	7 44	15 59
8	L	22 41,6		182 04,2		11 51 56	7 45	15 58
9	M	22 47,8		181 57,6		11 52 23	7 46	15 58
10	M	22 53,5		181 50,9		11 52 50	7 47	15 58
11	J	22 58,8	0,2	181 44,1		11 53 17	7 48	15 58
12	V	23 03,6		181 37,2		11 53 45	7 49	15 58
13	S	23 07,9		181 30,2		11 54 13	7 50	15 58
14	D	23 11,8		181 23,1		11 54 42	7 51	15 58
15	L	23 15,3		181 16,0		11 55 10	7 52	15 58
16	M	23 18,2	0,1	181 08,7		11 55 39	7 53	15 59
17	M	23 20,7		181 01,5		11 56 08	7 53	15 59
18	J	23 22,8		180 54,1		11 56 38	7 54	15 59
19	V	23 24,3		180 46,8	14,995	11 57 07	7 55	15 59
20	S	23 25,4		180 39,4		11 57 37	7 56	16 00
21	D	23 26,1	0,0	180 31,9		11 58 07	7 56	16 00
22	L	23 26,2		180 24,5		11 58 37	7 56	16 01
23	M	23 25,9		180 17,0		11 59 07	7 57	16 01
24	M	23 25,1		180 09,5		11 59 37	7 57	16 02
25	J	23 23,9		180 02,1		12 00 06	7 58	16 03
26	V	23 22,1	0,1	179 54,6		12 00 36	7 58	16 03
27	S	23 19,9		179 47,2		12 01 06	7 58	16 04
28	D	23 17,3		179 39,8		12 01 35	7 58	16 05
29	L	23 14,1		179 32,4		12 02 05	7 58	16 06
30	M	23 10,6	0,2	179 25,1		12 02 34	7 59	16 07
31	M	23 06,5S		179 17,9		12 03 03	7 59	16 08

Extracts from *L'Almanach du Marin Breton*

Year N + 1

Janvier

Janv.		Déclinaison à 0 h U.T. (° ')	d (')	AHvo à 0 h U.T. (° ')	V (o)	T. Pass. U.T. (h. mn. s.)	Lever U.T. (h. mn.)	Coucher U.T. (h. mn.)
1	J	23 02,0S		179 10,7		12 03 31	7 59	16 09
2	V	22 57,0	0,2	179 03,6		12 04 00	7 58	16 10
3	S	22 51,6		178 56,6	14,995	12 04 27	7 58	16 11
4	D	22 45,7		178 49,7		12 04 55	7 58	16 12
5	L	22 39,3		178 42,9		12 05 22	7 58	16 13
6	M	22 32,5	0,3	178 36,2		12 05 49	7 58	16 14
7	M	22 25,3		178 29,6		12 06 15	7 57	16 15
8	J	22 17,6		178 23,2		12 06 40	7 57	16 17
9	V	22 09,5		178 16,9		12 07 05	7 56	16 18
10	S	22 00,9		178 10,7		12 07 30	7 56	16 19
11	D	21 52,0		178 04,6	14,996	12 07 53	7 55	16 21
12	L	21 42,5	0,4	177 58,7		12 08 17	7 55	16 22
13	M	21 32,7		177 53,0		12 08 39	7 54	16 23
14	M	21 22,5		177 47,4		12 09 01	7 54	16 25
15	J	21 11,8		177 42,0		12 09 23	7 53	16 26
16	V	21 00,8		177 36,7		12 09 44	7 52	16 28
17	S	20 49,3	0,5	177 31,6		12 10 04	7 51	16 29
18	D	20 37,4		177 26,7		12 10 23	7 50	16 31
19	L	20 25,2		177 21,9		12 10 42	7 49	16 32
20	M	20 12,5		177 17,4	14,997	12 11 00	7 48	16 34
21	M	19 59,5		177 13,0		12 11 17	7 47	16 36
22	J	19 46,1		177 08,8		12 11 33	7 46	16 37
23	V	19 32,4	0,6	177 04,7		12 11 49	7 45	16 39
24	S	19 18,2		177 00,9		12 12 04	7 44	16 40
25	D	19 03,8		176 57,3		12 12 18	7 43	16 42
26	L	18 48,9		176 53,8		12 12 31	7 42	16 44
27	M	18 33,7		176 50,6		12 12 44	7 41	16 45
28	M	18 18,2		176 47,5	14,998	12 12 56	7 39	16 47
29	J	18 02,4	0,7	176 44,7		12 13 07	7 38	16 49
30	V	17 46,2		176 42,0		12 13 17	7 37	16 50
31	S	17 29,7S		176 39,6		12 13 26	7 35	16 52

Février

Fév.		Déclinaison à 0 h U.T. (° ')	d (')	AHvo à 0 h U.T. (° ')	V (o)	T. Pass. U.T. (h. mn. s.)	Lever U.T. (h. mn.)	Coucher U.T. (h. mn.)
1	D	17 13,0S		176 37,4		12 13 35	7 34	16 54
2	L	16 55,9	0,7	176 35,4		12 13 42	7 32	16 56
3	M	16 38,5		176 33,5	14,999	12 13 49	7 31	16 57
4	M	16 20,8		176 31,9		12 13 55	7 29	16 59
5	J	16 02,8		176 30,5		12 14 00	7 28	17 01
6	V	15 44,6		176 29,4		12 14 05	7 26	17 02
7	S	15 26,1		176 28,4		12 14 08	7 25	17 04
8	D	15 07,3		176 27,6		12 14 11	7 23	17 06
9	L	14 48,3	0,8	176 27,0		12 14 13	7 21	17 08
10	M	14 29,0		176 26,6	15,000	12 14 14	7 20	17 09
11	M	14 09,5		176 26,5		12 14 14	7 18	17 11
12	J	13 49,8		176 26,5		12 14 14	7 16	17 13
13	V	13 29,8		176 26,7		12 14 13	7 15	17 15
14	S	13 09,6		176 27,1		12 14 11	7 13	17 16
15	D	12 49,2		176 27,6		12 14 08	7 11	17 18
16	L	12 28,6		176 28,4		12 14 05	7 09	17 20
17	M	12 07,7		176 29,3		12 14 01	7 07	17 21
18	M	11 46,7		176 30,4		12 13 56	7 06	17 23
19	J	11 25,5		176 31,7		12 13 50	7 04	17 25
20	V	11 04,1		176 33,1	15,001	12 13 44	7 02	17 27
21	S	10 42,6		176 34,7		12 13 38	7 00	17 28
22	D	10 20,9	0,9	176 36,4		12 13 30	6 58	17 30
23	L	9 59,0		176 38,3		12 13 22	6 56	17 32
24	M	9 36,9		176 40,4		12 13 14	6 54	17 33
25	M	9 14,7		176 42,6		12 13 05	6 52	17 35
26	J	8 52,4		176 44,9		12 12 55	6 50	17 37
27	V	8 30,0		176 47,4	15,002	12 12 45	6 48	17 38
28	S	8 07,4S		176 50,1		12 12 34	6 46	17 40

Mars

Mars		Déclinaison à 0 h U.T. (° ')	d (')	AHvo à 0 h U.T. (° ')	V (o)	T. Pass. U.T. (h. mn. s.)	Lever U.T. (h. mn.)	Coucher U.T. (h. mn.)
1	D	7 44,7S		176 52,8		12 12 23	6 44	17 42
2	L	7 21,9		176 55,7		12 12 11	6 42	17 43
3	M	6 59,0		176 58,7		12 11 59	6 40	17 45
4	M	6 35,9		177 01,9	15,002	12 11 46	6 38	17 47
5	J	6 12,8		177 05,1		12 11 33	6 36	17 48
6	V	5 49,7		177 08,5		12 11 19	6 34	17 50
7	S	5 26,4		177 12,0		12 11 05	6 31	17 52
8	D	5 03,0		177 15,6		12 10 50	6 29	17 53
9	L	4 39,6		177 19,3		12 10 35	6 27	17 55
10	M	4 16,2		177 23,1		12 10 20	6 25	17 56
11	M	3 52,7		177 26,9		12 10 04	6 23	17 58
12	J	3 29,1		177 30,9		12 09 48	6 21	18 00
13	V	3 05,5		177 34,9		12 09 32	6 19	18 01
14	S	2 41,9		177 39,0		12 09 15	6 17	18 03
15	D	2 18,2		177 43,2		12 08 59	6 14	18 05
16	L	1 54,5	1,0	177 47,4		12 08 42	6 12	18 06
17	M	1 30,8		177 51,7		12 08 24	6 10	18 08
18	M	1 07,1		177 56,1		12 08 07	6 08	18 09
19	J	0 43,4		178 00,4	15,003	12 07 49	6 06	18 11
20	V	0 19,7S		178 04,8		12 07 32	6 04	18 13
21	S	0 04,0N		178 09,3		12 07 14	6 01	18 14
22	D	0 27,7		178 13,7		12 06 56	5 59	18 16
23	L	0 51,4		178 18,2		12 06 38	5 57	18 17
24	M	1 15,1		178 22,7		12 06 20	5 55	18 19
25	M	1 38,7		178 27,2		12 06 02	5 53	18 20
26	J	2 02,3		178 31,7		12 05 44	5 50	18 22
27	V	2 25,8		178 36,3		12 05 26	5 48	18 24
28	S	2 49,3		178 40,8		12 05 08	5 46	18 25
29	D	3 12,8		178 45,3		12 04 50	5 44	18 27
30	L	3 36,1		178 49,8		12 04 32	5 42	18 28
31	M	3 59,5N		178 54,3		12 04 14	5 40	18 30

Avril

Avril		Déclinaison à 0 h U.T. (° ')	d (')	AHvo à 0 h U.T. (° ')	V (o)	T. Pass. U.T. (h. mn. s.)	Lever U.T. (h. mn.)	Coucher U.T. (h. mn.)
1	M	4 22,7N		178 58,7		12 03 56	5 37	18 31
2	J	4 45,8	1,0	179 03,2		12 03 38	5 35	18 33
3	V	5 08,9		179 07,6		12 03 21	5 33	18 35
4	S	5 31,9		179 12,0		12 03 03	5 31	18 36
5	D	5 54,8		179 16,4		12 02 46	5 29	18 38
6	L	6 17,5		179 20,7		12 02 29	5 27	18 39
7	M	6 40,2		179 25,0		12 02 12	5 25	18 41
8	M	7 02,7		179 29,2	15,003	12 01 55	5 22	18 42
9	J	7 25,2		179 33,4		12 01 38	5 20	18 44
10	V	7 47,5		179 37,5		12 01 22	5 18	18 46
11	S	8 09,6		179 41,5		12 01 06	5 16	18 47
12	D	8 31,6	0,9	179 45,5		12 00 50	5 14	18 49
13	L	8 53,5		179 49,4		12 00 35	5 12	18 50
14	M	9 15,3		179 53,2		12 00 19	5 10	18 52
15	M	9 36,9		179 57,0		12 00 05	5 08	18 53
16	J	9 58,3		180 00,6		11 59 50	5 06	18 55
17	V	10 19,5		180 04,2		11 59 36	5 04	18 57
18	S	10 40,6		180 07,7		11 59 23	5 02	18 58
19	D	11 01,6		180 11,0		11 59 09	5 00	19 00
20	L	11 22,3		180 14,3		11 58 57	4 58	19 01
21	M	11 42,8		180 17,4		11 58 44	4 56	19 03
22	D	12 03,2		180 20,4	15,002	11 58 32	4 54	19 04
23	J	12 23,4		180 23,4		11 58 21	4 52	19 06
24	M	12 43,3		180 26,2		11 58 10	4 50	19 07
25	M	13 03,1	0,8	180 28,8		11 57 59	4 48	19 09
26	D	13 22,6		180 31,4		11 57 49	4 46	19 11
27	L	13 41,9		180 33,8		11 57 40	4 44	19 12
28	M	14 01,0		180 36,1		11 57 31	4 42	19 14
29	M	14 19,9		180 38,3	15,001	11 57 23	4 41	19 15
30	J	14 38,5N		180 40,4		11 57 15	4 39	19 17

Mai		Déclinaison à 0h U.T.	d	AHvo à 0h U.T.	V	T. Pass. U.T.	Lever U.T.	Coucher U.T.	Juin		Déclinaison à 0h U.T.	d	AHvo à 0h U.T.	V	T. Pass. U.T.	Lever U.T.	Coucher U.T.
		o '	'	o '	o	h. mn. s.	h. mn.	h. mn.			o '	'	o '	o	h. mn. s.	h. mn.	h. mn.
1	V	14 56,9N	0,8	180 42,3		11 57 07	4 37	19 18	1	L	21 59,7N		180 34,2		11 57 48	3 56	20 00
2	S	15 15,0		180 44,1		11 57 00	4 35	19 20	2	M	22 07,8		180 31,9		11 57 57	3 55	20 01
3	D	15 32,9		180 45,8		11 56 54	4 33	19 21	3	M	22 15,5		180 29,6		11 58 07	3 55	20 02
4	L	15 50,5		180 47,3	15,001	11 56 48	4 32	19 23	4	J	22 22,8	0,3	180 27,1		11 58 17	3 54	20 03
5	M	16 07,9		180 48,7		11 56 42	4 30	19 24	5	V	22 29,8		180 24,5		11 58 27	3 54	20 04
6	M	16 25,0	0,7	180 50,0		11 56 38	4 28	19 26	6	S	22 36,3		180 21,9		11 58 38	3 53	20 05
7	J	16 41,8		180 51,1		11 56 33	4 27	19 27	7	D	22 42,5		180 19,2		11 58 49	3 52	20 06
8	V	16 58,3		180 52,1		11 56 30	4 25	19 29	8	L	22 48,3		180 16,4		11 59 00	3 52	20 06
9	S	17 14,6		180 53,0		11 56 27	4 23	19 30	9	M	22 53,6	0,2	180 13,6		11 59 11	3 52	20 07
10	D	17 30,6		180 53,7		11 56 24	4 22	19 32	10	M	22 58,6		180 10,7		11 59 23	3 51	20 08
11	L	17 46,2		180 54,3		11 56 22	4 20	19 33	11	J	23 03,1		180 07,7		11 59 35	3 51	20 08
12	M	18 01,6		180 54,7		11 56 20	4 19	19 35	12	V	23 07,3		180 04,7		11 59 47	3 51	20 09
13	M	18 16,7		180 55,0	15,000	11 56 20	4 17	19 36	13	S	23 11,0		180 01,6		12 00 00	3 51	20 10
14	J	18 31,4	0,6	180 55,2		11 56 19	4 16	19 38	14	D	23 14,3		179 58,5		12 00 13	3 50	20 10
15	V	18 45,9		180 55,2		11 56 20	4 15	19 39	15	L	23 17,3	0,1	179 55,3	14,998	12 00 25	3 50	20 11
16	S	19 00,0		180 55,0		11 56 20	4 13	19 40	16	M	23 19,8		179 52,2		12 00 38	3 50	20 11
17	D	19 13,8		180 54,7		11 56 22	4 12	19 42	17	M	23 21,9		179 48,9		12 00 51	3 50	20 12
18	L	19 27,3		180 54,3		11 56 24	4 11	19 43	18	J	23 23,6		179 45,7		12 01 04	3 50	20 12
19	M	19 40,5		180 53,7		11 56 27	4 09	19 45	19	V	23 24,8		179 42,4		12 01 17	3 50	20 12
20	M	19 53,3		180 53,0		11 56 30	4 08	19 46	20	S	23 25,7		179 39,1		12 01 30	3 50	20 13
21	J	20 05,8	0,5	180 52,1		11 56 33	4 07	19 47	21	D	23 26,1	0,0	179 35,9		12 01 43	3 51	20 13
22	V	20 17,9		180 51,1		11 56 38	4 06	19 48	22	L	23 26,2		179 32,6		12 01 56	3 51	20 13
23	S	20 29,7		180 50,0		11 56 43	4 04	19 50	23	M	23 25,8		179 29,3		12 02 09	3 51	20 13
24	D	20 41,2		180 48,7		11 56 48	4 03	19 51	24	M	23 25,0		179 26,0		12 02 22	3 51	20 13
25	L	20 52,3	14,999	180 47,3		11 56 54	4 02	19 52	25	J	23 23,8		179 22,8		12 02 35	3 52	20 13
26	M	21 03,0		180 45,8		11 57 00	4 01	19 53	26	V	23 22,2	0,1	179 19,6		12 02 48	3 52	20 13
27	M	21 13,4		180 44,1		11 57 07	4 00	19 55	27	S	23 20,2		179 16,4		12 03 01	3 53	20 13
28	J	21 23,4	0,4	180 42,4		11 57 14	3 59	19 56	28	D	23 17,7		179 13,3		12 03 13	3 53	20 13
29	V	21 33,0		180 40,5		11 57 22	3 59	19 57	29	L	23 14,9		179 10,2		12 03 25	3 54	20 13
30	S	21 42,3		180 38,5		11 57 30	3 58	19 58	30	M	23 11,6N	0,2	179 07,2		12 03 37	3 54	20 13
31	D	21 51,2N		180 36,4	14,998	11 57 39	3 58	19 59									

Juillet		Déclinaison à 0h U.T.	d	AHvo à 0h U.T.	V	T. Pass. U.T.	Lever U.T.	Coucher U.T.	Août		Déclinaison à 0h U.T.	d	AHvo à 0h U.T.	V	T. Pass. U.T.	Lever U.T.	Coucher U.T.
		o '	'	o '	o	h. mn. s.	h. mn.	h. mn.			o '	'	o '	o	h. mn. s.	h. mn.	h. mn.
1	M	23 08,0N		179 04,2		12 03 49	3 55	20 12	1	S	18 07,2N	0,6	178 24,6		12 06 20	4 29	19 43
2	J	23 03,9		179 01,3		12 04 00	3 55	20 12	2	D	17 52,0		178 25,5		12 06 16	4 30	19 41
3	V	22 59,4	0,2	178 58,5		12 04 12	3 56	20 12	3	L	17 36,6		178 26,6		12 06 11	4 32	19 40
4	S	22 54,6		178 55,8		12 04 22	3 57	20 11	4	M	17 20,9		178 27,8		12 06 06	4 33	19 38
5	D	22 49,3		178 53,1	14,998	12 04 33	3 58	20 11	5	M	17 05,0		178 29,2	15,001	12 06 00	4 35	19 36
6	L	22 43,6		178 50,5		12 04 43	3 58	20 10	6	J	16 48,7		178 30,7		12 05 54	4 36	19 35
7	M	22 37,6		178 48,0		12 04 53	3 59	20 10	7	V	16 32,2	0,7	178 32,4		12 05 47	4 37	19 33
8	M	22 31,1		178 45,6		12 05 02	4 00	20 09	8	S	16 15,4		178 34,3		12 05 39	4 39	19 31
9	J	22 24,3	0,3	178 43,3		12 05 11	4 01	20 09	9	D	15 58,3		178 36,3		12 05 31	4 40	19 30
10	V	22 17,1		178 41,1		12 05 20	4 02	20 08	10	L	15 41,0		178 38,4		12 05 22	4 42	19 28
11	S	22 09,5		178 39,0		12 05 28	4 03	20 07	11	M	15 23,5		178 40,7		12 05 12	4 43	19 26
12	D	22 01,5		178 37,1		12 05 36	4 04	20 07	12	M	15 05,7		178 43,1		12 05 03	4 45	19 24
13	L	21 53,1		178 35,2		12 05 43	4 05	20 06	13	J	14 47,6		178 45,6		12 04 52	4 46	19 22
14	M	21 44,4		178 33,4		12 05 50	4 06	20 05	14	V	14 29,4		178 48,3		12 04 41	4 48	19 21
15	M	21 35,2	0,4	178 31,8	14,999	12 05 56	4 07	20 04	15	S	14 10,8		178 51,1	15,002	12 04 30	4 49	19 19
16	J	21 25,8		178 30,3		12 06 02	4 08	20 03	16	D	13 52,1		178 54,1		12 04 18	4 51	19 17
17	V	21 15,9		178 28,9		12 06 07	4 09	20 02	17	L	13 33,1	0,8	178 57,2		12 04 05	4 52	19 15
18	S	21 05,7		178 27,6		12 06 12	4 11	20 01	18	M	13 14,0		179 00,4		12 03 52	4 54	19 13
19	D	20 55,1		178 26,5		12 06 16	4 12	20 00	19	M	12 54,6		179 03,7		12 03 38	4 55	19 11
20	L	20 44,2		178 25,5		12 06 20	4 13	19 59	20	J	12 35,0		179 07,1		12 03 24	4 57	19 09
21	M	20 32,9		178 24,6		12 06 23	4 14	19 58	21	V	12 15,2		179 10,7		12 03 10	4 58	19 07
22	M	20 21,3	0,5	178 23,8		12 06 26	4 16	19 57	22	S	11 55,2		179 14,3		12 02 55	5 00	19 05
23	J	20 09,4		178 23,2		12 06 28	4 17	19 55	23	D	11 35,0		179 18,1		12 02 40	5 01	19 03
24	V	19 57,1		178 22,8		12 06 30	4 18	19 54	24	L	11 14,7		179 22,0		12 02 24	5 03	19 01
25	S	19 44,5		178 22,5	15,000	12 06 30	4 19	19 53	25	M	10 54,1		179 26,0		12 02 08	5 04	18 59
26	D	19 31,5		178 22,3		12 06 31	4 21	19 51	26	M	10 33,4		179 30,1	15,003	12 01 51	5 06	18 57
27	L	19 18,2		178 22,3		12 06 31	4 22	19 50	27	J	10 12,5	0,9	179 34,4		12 01 34	5 07	18 55
28	M	19 04,6		178 22,5		12 06 30	4 23	19 49	28	V	9 51,5		179 38,7		12 01 16	5 09	18 53
29	M	18 50,7	0,6	178 22,8		12 06 28	4 25	19 47	29	S	9 30,3		179 43,1		12 00 59	5 10	18 51
30	J	18 36,5		178 23,2		12 06 26	4 26	19 46	30	D	9 09,0		179 47,6		12 00 40	5 12	18 49
31	V	18 22,0N		178 23,8	15,001	12 06 23	4 28	19 44	31	L	8 47,5N		179 52,2		12 00 22	5 13	18 47

Extracts from *L'Almanach du Marin Breton*

Year N + 1

Sept.		Déclinaison à 0 h U.T. (° ')	d (')	AHvo à 0 h U.T. (° ')	V (o)	T. Pass. U.T. (h. mn. s.)	Lever U.T. (h. mn.)	Coucher U.T. (h. mn.)
1	M	8 25,9N		179 56,9		12 00 03	5 15	18 45
2	M	8 04,1		180 01,6		11 59 44	5 16	18 42
3	J	7 42,2		180 06,5		11 59 24	5 18	18 40
4	V	7 20,2		180 11,4	15,003	11 59 05	5 19	18 38
5	S	6 58,1	0,9	180 16,3		11 58 45	5 20	18 36
6	D	6 35,8		180 21,4		11 58 24	5 22	18 34
7	L	6 13,5		180 26,5		11 58 04	5 23	18 32
8	M	5 51,0		180 31,6		11 57 43	5 25	18 30
9	M	5 28,5		180 36,8		11 57 22	5 26	18 27
10	J	5 05,8		180 42,0		11 57 02	5 28	18 25
11	V	4 43,1		180 47,3		11 56 40	5 29	18 23
12	S	4 20,3		180 52,5		11 56 19	5 31	18 21
13	D	3 57,4		180 57,8		11 55 58	5 32	18 19
14	L	3 34,4		181 03,1		11 55 37	5 34	18 16
15	M	3 11,4		181 08,5		11 55 16	5 35	18 14
16	M	2 48,3		181 13,8		11 54 54	5 37	18 12
17	J	2 25,2		181 19,1	15,004	11 54 33	5 38	18 10
18	V	2 02,0		181 24,5		11 54 12	5 40	18 08
19	S	1 38,7		181 29,8		11 53 50	5 41	18 05
20	D	1 15,5	1,0	181 35,1		11 53 29	5 43	18 03
21	L	0 52,2		181 40,4		11 53 08	5 44	18 01
22	M	0 28,8		181 45,7		11 52 47	5 46	17 59
23	M	0 05,5N		181 51,0		11 52 26	5 47	17 57
24	J	0 17,9S		181 56,2		11 52 05	5 49	17 54
25	V	0 41,3		182 01,4		11 51 44	5 50	17 52
26	S	1 04,6		182 06,6		11 51 23	5 52	17 50
27	D	1 28,0		182 11,7		11 51 03	5 53	17 48
28	L	1 51,4		182 16,8		11 50 43	5 55	17 46
29	M	2 14,7		182 21,8	15,003	11 50 23	5 56	17 43
30	M	2 38,0S		182 26,8		11 50 03	5 58	17 41

Oct.		Déclinaison à 0 h U.T. (° ')	d (')	AHvo à 0 h U.T. (° ')	V (o)	T. Pass. U.T. (h. mn. s.)	Lever U.T. (h. mn.)	Coucher U.T. (h. mn.)
1	J	3 01,3S		182 31,7		11 49 43	6 00	17 39
2	V	3 24,6		182 36,6		11 49 24	6 01	17 37
3	S	3 47,8		182 41,4		11 49 05	6 03	17 35
4	D	4 11,0		182 46,1		11 48 47	6 04	17 33
5	L	4 34,1	1,0	182 50,7		11 48 28	6 06	17 30
6	M	4 57,2		182 55,2		11 48 10	6 07	17 28
7	M	5 20,2		182 59,7	15,003	11 47 53	6 09	17 26
8	J	5 43,2		183 04,0		11 47 36	6 10	17 24
9	V	6 06,0		183 08,2		11 47 19	6 12	17 22
10	S	6 28,8		183 12,4		11 47 03	6 13	17 20
11	D	6 51,5		183 16,3		11 46 47	6 15	17 18
12	L	7 14,1		183 20,2		11 46 32	6 17	17 16
13	M	7 36,7		183 24,0		11 46 17	6 18	17 14
14	M	7 59,1		183 27,6		11 46 03	6 20	17 11
15	J	8 21,4		183 31,1		11 45 49	6 21	17 09
16	V	8 43,6		183 34,4		11 45 36	6 23	17 07
17	S	9 05,6		183 37,6		11 45 24	6 25	17 05
18	D	9 27,6	0,9	183 40,6	15,002	11 45 12	6 26	17 03
19	L	9 49,4		183 43,5		11 45 01	6 28	17 01
20	M	10 11,0		183 46,2		11 44 50	6 29	16 59
21	M	10 32,6		183 48,8		11 44 40	6 31	16 57
22	J	10 53,9		183 51,2		11 44 31	6 33	16 54
23	V	11 15,1		183 53,4		11 44 22	6 34	16 54
24	S	11 36,1		183 55,5		11 44 14	6 36	16 52
25	D	11 57,0		183 57,4		11 44 07	6 38	16 50
26	L	12 17,7		183 59,1	15,001	11 44 00	6 39	16 48
27	M	12 38,1		184 00,7		11 43 54	6 41	16 46
28	M	12 58,4		184 02,1		11 43 49	6 43	16 44
29	J	13 18,5	0,8	184 03,2		11 43 45	6 44	16 43
30	V	13 38,4		184 04,2		11 43 41	6 46	16 41
31	S	13 58,0S		184 05,1	15,000	11 43 38	6 47	16 39

Nov.		Déclinaison à 0 h U.T. (° ')	d (')	AHvo à 0 h U.T. (° ')	V (o)	T. Pass. U.T. (h. mn. s.)	Lever U.T. (h. mn.)	Coucher U.T. (h. mn.)
1	D	14 17,4S		184 05,7		11 43 36	6 49	16 37
2	L	14 36,6		184 06,1		11 43 35	6 51	16 36
3	M	14 55,6	0,8	184 06,3	15,000	11 43 35	6 53	16 34
4	M	15 14,3		184 06,4		11 43 35	6 54	16 32
5	J	15 32,8		184 06,2		11 43 36	6 56	16 31
6	V	15 51,0		184 05,8		11 43 38	6 57	16 29
7	S	16 08,9		184 05,2		11 43 41	6 59	16 28
8	D	16 26,6		184 04,4		11 43 44	7 01	16 26
9	L	16 44,0		184 03,4	14,999	11 43 49	7 02	16 25
10	M	17 01,1	0,7	184 02,1		11 43 54	7 04	16 23
11	M	17 17,9		184 00,7		11 44 00	7 06	16 22
12	J	17 34,5		183 59,0		11 44 08	7 07	16 20
13	V	17 50,7		183 57,1		11 44 16	7 09	16 19
14	S	18 06,6		183 55,0		11 44 24	7 11	16 18
15	D	18 22,2		183 52,7		11 44 34	7 12	16 16
16	L	18 37,5		183 50,2	14,998	11 44 45	7 14	16 15
17	M	18 52,5		183 47,4		11 44 56	7 16	16 14
18	M	19 07,1	0,6	183 44,5		11 45 08	7 17	16 13
19	J	19 21,4		183 41,3		11 45 21	7 19	16 12
20	V	19 35,3		183 37,9		11 45 35	7 20	16 10
21	S	19 48,9		183 34,3		11 45 50	7 22	16 09
22	D	20 02,1		183 30,6		11 46 05	7 23	16 08
23	L	20 15,0		183 26,6	14,997	11 46 22	7 25	16 07
24	M	20 27,5	0,5	183 22,4		11 46 39	7 26	16 06
25	M	20 39,6		183 18,0		11 46 57	7 28	16 06
26	J	20 51,3		183 13,5		11 47 15	7 29	16 05
27	V	21 02,6		183 08,8		11 47 34	7 31	16 04
28	S	21 13,5		183 03,9		11 47 54	7 32	16 03
29	D	21 24,1	0,4	182 58,8	14,996	11 48 15	7 34	16 03
30	L	21 34,2S		182 53,6		11 48 36	7 35	16 02

Déc.		Déclinaison à 0 h U.T. (° ')	d (')	AHvo à 0 h U.T. (° ')	V (o)	T. Pass. U.T. (h. mn. s.)	Lever U.T. (h. mn.)	Coucher U.T. (h. mn.)
1	M	21 43,9S		182 48,2		11 48 58	7 36	16 01
2	M	21 53,2	0,4	182 42,6		11 49 21	7 38	16 01
3	J	22 02,1		182 36,9		11 49 44	7 39	16 00
4	V	22 10,5		182 31,0	14,996	11 50 08	7 40	16 00
5	S	22 18,6		182 25,0		11 50 32	7 41	15 59
6	D	22 26,2	0,3	182 18,8		11 50 57	7 43	15 59
7	L	22 33,3		182 12,5		11 51 23	7 44	15 59
8	M	22 40,0		182 06,0		11 51 49	7 45	15 58
9	M	22 46,3		181 59,5		11 52 15	7 46	15 58
10	J	22 52,1		181 52,8		11 52 42	7 47	15 58
11	V	22 57,5	0,2	181 46,0		11 53 10	7 48	15 58
12	S	23 02,4		181 39,1		11 53 37	7 49	15 58
13	D	23 06,9		181 32,1		11 54 06	7 50	15 58
14	L	23 10,9		181 25,0		11 54 34	7 51	15 58
15	M	23 14,4		181 17,9		11 55 03	7 52	15 58
16	M	23 17,5	0,1	181 10,6		11 55 32	7 52	15 58
17	J	23 20,2		181 03,3		11 56 01	7 53	15 59
18	V	23 22,3		180 56,0		11 56 31	7 54	15 59
19	S	23 24,0		180 48,6	14,995	11 57 00	7 55	15 59
20	D	23 25,2		180 41,2		11 57 30	7 55	16 00
21	L	23 26,0		180 33,7		11 58 00	7 56	16 00
22	M	23 26,2	0,0	180 26,2		11 58 30	7 56	16 01
23	M	23 26,2		180 18,8		11 59 00	7 57	16 01
24	J	23 25,4		180 11,3		11 59 30	7 57	16 02
25	V	23 24,2		180 03,8		12 00 00	7 58	16 03
26	S	23 22,5		179 56,4		12 00 29	7 58	16 03
27	D	23 20,5	0,1	179 49,0		12 00 59	7 58	16 04
28	L	23 18,0		179 41,6		12 01 28	7 58	16 05
29	M	23 15,0		179 34,3		12 01 58	7 58	16 06
30	M	23 11,5	0,2	179 27,0		12 02 27	7 59	16 07
31	J	23 07,6S		179 19,8		12 02 55	7 59	16 07

Monday 20 July - Year N + 1

Heure U.T.	Point vernal AHso	VÉNUS AHvo		D	MARS AHvo		D	JUPITER AHvo		D	SATURNE AHvo		D	Heure U.T.
00	297 34,4	207 05,9	N 22	43,2	197 33,6	N 23	50,0	298 49,1	S 2	01,3	265 55,0	N 10	11,6	00
01	312 36,8	222 05,1	22	43,3	212 34,3	23	49,9	313 51,5	2	01,3	280 57,4	10	11,7	01
02	327 39,3	237 04,3	22	43,4	227 34,9	23	49,8	328 54,0	2	01,4	295 59,7	10	11,7	02
03	342 41,8	252 03,5	22	43,5	242 35,6	23	49,7	343 56,5	2	01,4	311 02,1	10	11,7	03
04	357 44,2	267 02,7	22	43,6	257 36,2	23	49,6	358 59,0	2	01,4	326 04,5	10	11,7	04
05	12 46,7	282 01,9	22	43,7	272 36,9	23	49,5	14 01,4	2	01,4	341 06,8	10	11,8	05
06	27 49,2	297 01,1	N 22	43,8	287 37,5	N 23	49,4	29 03,9	S 2	01,4	356 09,2	N 10	11,8	06
07	42 51,6	312 00,3	22	43,9	302 38,1	23	49,3	44 06,4	2	01,5	11 11,5	10	11,8	07
08	57 54,1	326 59,5	22	44,0	317 38,8	23	49,2	59 08,9	2	01,5	26 13,9	10	11,9	08
09	72 56,6	341 58,7	22	44,1	332 39,4	23	49,2	74 11,3	2	01,5	41 16,2	10	11,9	09
10	87 59,0	356 57,9	22	44,2	347 40,1	23	49,1	89 13,8	2	01,5	56 18,6	10	11,9	10
11	103 01,5	11 57,1	22	44,3	2 40,7	23	49,0	104 16,3	2	01,5	71 20,9	10	11,9	11
12	118 03,9	26 56,3	N 22	44,3	17 41,4	N 23	48,9	119 18,8	S 2	01,6	86 23,3	N 10	12,0	12
13	133 06,4	41 55,5	22	44,4	32 42,0	23	48,8	134 21,2	2	01,6	101 25,6	10	12,0	13
14	148 08,9	56 54,7	22	44,5	47 42,7	23	48,7	149 23,7	2	01,6	116 28,0	10	12,0	14
15	163 11,3	71 53,9	22	44,6	62 43,3	23	48,6	164 26,2	2	01,6	131 30,3	10	12,1	15
16	178 13,8	86 53,1	22	44,7	77 44,0	23	48,5	179 28,7	2	01,6	146 32,7	10	12,1	16
17	193 16,3	101 52,3	22	44,8	92 44,6	23	48,4	194 31,2	2	01,7	161 35,1	10	12,1	17
18	208 18,7	116 51,5	N 22	44,9	107 45,3	N 23	48,3	209 33,6	S 2	01,7	176 37,4	N 10	12,1	18
19	223 21,2	131 50,7	22	44,9	122 45,9	23	48,2	224 36,1	2	01,7	191 39,8	10	12,2	19
20	238 23,7	146 49,9	22	45,0	137 46,5	23	48,1	239 38,6	2	01,7	206 42,1	10	12,2	20
21	253 26,1	161 49,1	22	45,1	152 47,2	23	48,0	254 41,1	2	01,7	221 44,5	10	12,2	21
22	268 28,6	176 48,3	22	45,2	167 47,8	23	47,9	269 43,6	2	01,8	236 46,8	10	12,2	22
23	283 31,1	191 47,5	22	45,3	182 48,5	23	47,8	284 46,0	2	01,8	251 49,2	10	12,3	23
24	298 33,5	206 46,7	N 22	45,3	197 49,1	N 23	47,7	299 48,5	S 2	01,8	266 51,5	N 10	12,3	24

v = 0,8 d = 0,1	ϑ = 0,6 d = 0,1	v = 2,5 d = 0,0	v = 2,4 d = 0,0
mag. = -3,8 π = 0,1	mag. = +1,6 π = 0,1	mag. = -2,5 π = 0,0	mag. = +0,4 π = 0,0

Above, below and top right: Extracts from French Almanac *Ephémérides Nautiques* for Monday 20 July, year N+1; Tuesday 21 April, year N+1; and Monday 17 August, year N+1; giving the Greenwich Hour Angle of the First Point of Aries (Point Vernal AHso) and the Greenwich Hour Angle and Declination of four planets (AHao + D Venus etc) at a given UT (Heure UT).

Tuesday 21 April - Year N + 1

Heure U.T.	Point vernal AHso	VÉNUS AHvo		D	MARS AHvo		D	JUPITER AHvo		D	SATURNE AHvo		D	Heure U.T.
00	208 51,9	221 43,8	S 6	08,2	175 11,5	N 13	18,8	219 56,6	S 5	49,9	185 32,0	N 7	19,8	00
01	223 54,3	236 43,6	6	07,3	190 12,2	13	19,4	234 58,6	5	49,7	200 34,2	7	19,9	01
02	238 56,8	251 43,5	6	06,4	205 12,9	13	20,1	250 00,6	5	49,5	215 36,3	7	20,0	02
03	253 59,3	266 43,4	6	05,5	220 13,6	13	20,7	265 02,6	5	49,3	230 38,5	7	20,1	03
04	269 01,7	281 43,2	6	04,6	235 14,3	13	21,3	280 04,6	5	49,2	245 40,7	7	20,3	04
05	284 04,2	296 43,1	6	03,7	250 14,9	13	22,0	295 06,6	5	49,0	260 42,8	7	20,4	05
06	299 06,7	311 42,9	S 6	02,8	265 15,6	N 13	22,6	310 08,5	S 5	48,8	275 45,0	N 7	20,5	06
07	314 09,1	326 42,8	6	01,9	280 16,3	13	23,3	325 10,5	5	48,6	290 47,2	7	20,6	07
08	329 11,6	341 42,6	6	01,0	295 17,0	13	23,9	340 12,5	5	48,4	305 49,3	7	20,7	08
09	344 14,0	356 42,5	6	00,1	310 17,6	13	24,5	355 14,5	5	48,2	320 51,5	7	20,8	09
10	359 16,5	11 42,4	5	59,2	325 18,3	13	25,2	10 16,5	5	48,0	335 53,7	7	20,9	10
11	14 19,0	26 42,2	5	58,3	340 19,0	13	25,8	25 18,5	5	47,8	350 55,8	7	21,1	11
12	29 21,4	41 42,1	S 5	57,4	355 19,7	N 13	26,4	40 20,4	S 5	47,6	5 58,0	N 7	21,2	12
13	44 23,9	56 41,9	5	56,5	10 20,4	13	27,1	55 22,4	5	47,4	21 00,2	7	21,3	13
14	59 26,4	71 41,8	5	55,6	25 21,0	13	27,7	70 24,4	5	47,2	36 02,3	7	21,4	14
15	74 28,8	86 41,6	5	54,7	40 21,7	13	28,3	85 26,4	5	47,0	51 04,5	7	21,5	15
16	89 31,3	101 41,5	5	53,8	55 22,4	13	29,0	100 28,4	5	46,8	66 06,7	7	21,6	16
17	104 33,8	116 41,4	5	52,9	70 23,1	13	29,6	115 30,4	5	46,6	81 08,9	7	21,7	17
18	119 36,2	131 41,2	S 5	52,0	85 23,7	N 13	30,2	130 32,4	S 5	46,4	96 11,0	N 7	21,9	18
19	134 38,7	146 41,1	5	51,1	100 24,4	13	30,9	145 34,3	5	46,2	111 13,2	7	22,0	19
20	149 41,2	161 40,9	5	50,2	115 25,1	13	31,5	160 36,3	5	46,0	126 15,4	7	22,1	20
21	164 43,6	176 40,8	5	49,3	130 25,8	13	32,1	175 38,3	5	45,8	141 17,5	7	22,2	21
22	179 46,1	191 40,6	5	48,4	145 26,4	13	32,8	190 40,3	5	45,6	156 19,7	7	22,3	22
23	194 48,5	206 40,5	5	47,5	160 27,1	13	33,4	205 42,3	5	45,4	171 21,9	7	22,4	23
24	209 51,0	221 40,3	S 5	46,6	175 27,8	N 13	34,0	220 44,3	S 5	45,3	186 24,0	N 7	22,5	24

v = 0,1 d = 0,9	v = 0,7 d = 0,6	v = 2,0 d = 0,2	v = 2,2 d = 0,1
mag. = -4,1 π = 0,2	mag. = +1,3 π = 0,1	mag. = -2,0 π = 0,0	mag. = +0,5 π = 0,0

Monday 17 August - Year N + 1

Heure U.T.	Point vernal Aʰso	VÉNUS Aʰvo	D	MARS Aʰvo	D	JUPITER Aʰvo	D	SATURNE Aʰvo	D	Heure U.T.
00	325 10,3	198 17,6	N 19 39,6	205 21,3	N 21 34,9	327 39,9 S	2 42,2	292 53,1	N 10 17,2	00
01	340 12,7	213 16,9	19 38,9	220 22,1	21 34,6	342 42,6	2 42,3	307 55,6	10 17,2	01
02	355 15,2	228 16,2	19 38,3	235 22,8	21 34,3	357 45,3	2 42,4	322 58,1	10 17,2	02
03	10 17,7	243 15,4	19 37,7	250 23,6	21 34,0	12 48,0	2 42,5	338 00,5	10 17,2	03
04	25 20,1	258 14,7	19 37,0	265 24,4	21 33,7	27 50,6	2 42,6	353 03,0	10 17,2	04
05	40 22,6	273 14,0	19 36,4	280 25,1	21 33,4	42 53,3	2 42,7	8 05,5	10 17,2	05
06	55 25,0	288 13,3	N 19 35,8	295 25,9	N 21 33,1	57 56,0 S	2 42,8	23 07,9	N 10 17,2	06
07	70 27,5	303 12,6	19 35,1	310 26,6	21 32,8	72 58,6	2 42,9	38 10,4	10 17,1	07
08	85 30,0	318 11,9	19 34,5	325 27,4	21 32,5	88 01,3	2 43,0	53 12,9	10 17,1	08
09	100 32,4	333 11,2	19 33,8	340 28,1	21 32,2	103 04,0	2 43,1	68 15,3	10 17,1	09
10	115 34,9	348 10,5	19 33,2	355 28,9	21 31,9	118 06,7	2 43,2	83 17,8	10 17,1	10
11	130 37,4	3 09,7	19 32,6	10 29,6	21 31,6	133 09,3	2 43,3	98 20,3	10 17,1	11
12	145 39,8	18 09,0	N 19 31,9	25 30,4	N 21 31,3	148 12,0 S	2 43,4	113 22,7	N 10 17,1	12
13	160 42,3	33 08,3	19 31,3	40 31,2	21 30,9	163 14,7	2 43,5	128 25,2	10 17,1	13
14	175 44,8	48 07,6	19 30,6	55 31,9	21 30,6	178 17,4	2 43,6	143 27,7	10 17,1	14
15	190 47,2	63 06,9	19 30,0	70 32,7	21 30,3	193 20,0	2 43,7	158 30,1	10 17,0	15
16	205 49,7	78 06,2	19 29,3	85 33,4	21 30,0	208 22,7	2 43,8	173 32,6	10 17,0	16
17	220 52,1	93 05,5	19 28,7	100 34,2	21 29,7	223 25,4	2 43,9	188 35,1	10 17,0	17
18	235 54,6	108 04,8	N 19 28,0	115 34,9	N 21 29,4	238 28,0 S	2 44,0	203 37,5	N 10 17,0	18
19	250 57,1	123 04,1	19 27,4	130 35,7	21 29,1	253 30,7	2 44,1	218 40,0	10 17,0	19
20	265 59,5	138 03,4	19 26,7	145 36,5	21 28,8	268 33,4	2 44,2	233 42,5	10 17,0	20
21	281 02,0	153 02,7	19 26,1	160 37,2	21 28,5	283 36,1	2 44,3	248 45,0	10 17,0	21
22	296 04,5	168 02,0	19 25,4	175 38,0	21 28,2	298 38,7	2 44,4	263 47,4	10 17,0	22
23	311 06,9	183 01,2	19 24,7	190 38,7	21 27,9	313 41,4	2 44,5	278 49,9	10 16,9	23
24	326 09,4	198 00,5	N 19 24,1	205 39,5	N 21 27,6	328 44,1 S	2 44,6	293 52,4	N 10 16,9	24
		$v = 0,7$ $d = 0,6$		$v = 0,8$ $d = 0,3$		$v = 2,7$ $d = 0,1$		$v = 2,5$ $d = 0,0$		
		mag. $= -3,8$ $\pi = 0,1$		mag. $= +1,7$ $\pi = 0,1$		mag. $= -2,7$ $\pi = 0,0$		mag. $= +0,3$ $\pi = 0,0$		

A note about 'v'

The hourly variation in the planets' hour angle is usually assumed to be 15°/h (in other words the planets are visualised as moving round the Earth at an average speed of 15° an hour). v is the correction applied to establish the exact variation for a particular planet on a particular day.

Example

On 20 July in the year N + 1, the hour angles HA of the planets change at the following hourly rates:

$$HA\ Venus\ = 15° + v = 15° + 00'.8 = 15°.01333$$
$$HA\ Mars\ = 15° + v = 15° + 00'.6 = 15°.01000$$
$$HA\ Jupiter\ = 15° + v = 15° + 2'.5 = 15°.04167$$
$$HA\ Saturn\ = 15° + v = 15° + 2'.4 = 15°.04000$$

A note about 'd'

d is the hourly angular speed, on a given day, of a planet's declination D (d is properly described as a speed rather than a correction to a speed, like v). Note that d is governed by a sign not shown in the almanac.

Example

On 20 July in the year N + 1, the declination of the planets changes at the following rates:

Hourly variation of D for Venus $= d$ $= 00'.1$ $= 0°.00167$
Hourly variation of D for Mars $= -d$ $= -00'.1$ $= -0°.00167$
Hourly variation of D for Jupiter $= d$ $= 00'$
Hourly variation of D for Saturn $= d$ $= 00'$

(The sign is determined by whether the series of numbers increases or decreases)

Stars - Year N + 1

Constellation	Nom	Magnitude	Ascension verse						
			1er janv.	1er mars	1er mai	1er juil.	1er sept.	1er nov.	31 déc.
α Lion	Régulus	1,3	207 55,9	55,7	55,8	56,0	56,0	55,7	55,2
β Grande Ourse ...	Mérak	2,4	194 34,2	33,7	33,9	34,3	34,5	34,1	33,4
α Grande Ourse ...	Dubhe	2,0	194 06,0	05,4	05,6	06,1	06,3	06,0	05,1
δ Lion	Zosma	2,6	191 30,0	29,6	29,7	29,9	29,9	29,7	29,3
β Lion	Denebola	2,2	182 45,7	45,3	45,3	45,5	45,6	45,4	45,0
α Lyre	Véga	0,1	80 47,4	47,1	46,6	46,3	46,4	46,8	47,0
σ Sagittaire	Nunki	2,1	76 13,4	13,0	12,6	12,2	12,2	12,5	12,5
α Aigle	Altaïr	0,9	62 20,1	19,9	19,5	19,1	19,1	19,3	19,4
α Grand Chien .	Sirius	− 1,6	258 43,8	43,9	44,2	44,2	43,9	43,5	43,2
ε Grand Chien ..	Adhara	1,6	255 21,4	21,5	21,8	21,9	21,7	21,2	20,9
δ Grand Chien ..	Wezen	2,0	252 55,0	55,1	55,4	55,5	55,2	54,8	54,5
α Gémeaux	Castor	1,6	246 22,6	22,6	22,9	23,0	22,7	22,2	21,8
α Petit Chien ..	Procyon	0,5	245 11,8	11,8	12,0	12,1	11,9	11,5	11,1
β Gémeaux	Pollux	1,2	243 41,8	41,8	42,1	42,2	41,9	41,5	41,0

Stars - Year N + 1

Constellation	Nom	Magnitude	Déclinaison						
			1er janv.	1er mars	1er mai	1er juil.	1er sept.	1er nov.	31 déc.
α Lion	Régulus	1,3	N 11 58,5	58,4	58,5	58,5	58,5	58,4	58,2
β Grande Ourse ...	Mérak	2,4	N 56 23,3	23,4	23,7	23,7	23,5	23,2	23,0
α Grande Ourse ...	Dubhe	2,0	N 61 45,4	45,5	45,8	45,8	45,6	45,3	45,1
δ Lion	Zosma	2,6	N 20 31,9	31,9	32,0	32,1	32,0	31,9	31,7
β Lion	Denebola	2,2	N 14 34,9	34,8	34,9	35,0	35,0	34,8	34,6
α Lyre	Véga	0,1	N 38 47,0	46,8	46,8	47,1	47,3	47,3	47,1
σ Sagittaire	Nunki	2,1	S 26 17,8	17,8	17,8	17,8	17,8	17,8	17,8
α Aigle	Altaïr	0,9	N 8 51,9	51,7	51,8	52,0	52,1	52,1	52,0
α Grand Chien .	Sirius	− 1,6	S 16 43,0	43,1	43,1	43,0	42,8	42,8	43,0
ε Grand Chien ..	Adhara	1,6	S 28 58,3	58,5	58,5	58,3	58,1	58,1	58,4
δ Grand Chien ..	Wezen	2,0	S 26 23,5	23,8	23,8	23,6	23,3	23,4	23,6
α Gémeaux	Castor	1,6	N 31 53,4	53,5	53,5	53,5	53,4	53,3	53,3
α Petit Chien ..	Procyon	0,5	N 5 13,6	13,6	13,6	13,7	13,7	13,7	13,5
β Gémeaux	Pollux	1,2	N 28 01,7	01,7	01,8	01,8	01,7	01,6	01,6

CONCLUSION

Measurement leads through sextant sights; to optical corrections; to the true altitude Ho and the true azimuth or bearing Zv.

Calculation leads from the data in the nautical almanac, giving hour angle and declination; to the refinement of the hour angle and declination by interpolation (using the mathematical rule of three) in order to match the exact time of the sextant sight; to spherical trigonometry; to the calculated altitude Hc and the calculated bearing or azimuth Zc. This enables a comparison (at the bottom of the diagram) between Ho and Hc to obtain the intercept.

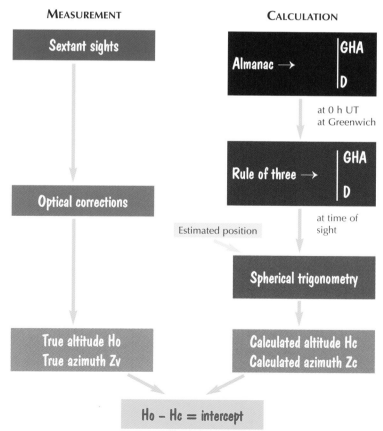

MAIN ABBREVIATIONS

Because the terms, notations, definitions and abbreviations you will encounter in books on astronavigation come both from the maritime world and from astronomy, they can be confusing. The main equivalents are therefore listed below.

Heavenly body
The Sun, Moon, planets, stars.

Pg
The geographical position of a heavenly body, also known as a heavenly body's footprint. Pg is a point on the Earth's surface along a line between the centre of a heavenly body and the centre of the Earth.

A
The letter marking either the trace of a heavenly body on the Earth's surface (in which case it is the same as Pg) or the heavenly body itself on the celestial sphere.

Z
The observer's zenith (the intersection of a vertical line through the observer's position with the celestial sphere) or the observer's position on Earth.

Angle Z; angle P
Angle Z is the internal angle of the triangle AZP.
Angle P is the angle at the pole, or the internal angle of the triangle ZPA.

Az = Zv
Az - true azimuth; Zv = true bearing or azimuth

Zc; Zn
Zc is the calculated bearing: Zc = angle Z in the morning, local time (heavenly body in the east); Zc = 360° - angle Z in the afternoon, local time (heavenly body in the west), where Z is the internal angle of the triangle AZP.
Zn = calculated bearing of a heavenly body in the British and American notation.

P, Pn or Ps
Used to designate the north or south poles, either on Earth or on the celestial sphere.

ZPA
Position triangle, also written PAZ or AZP.

GHA (= AHG)
Greenwich hour angle (angle horaire Greenwich): the angle between a heavenly body's meridian and the Greenwich meridian